TQM
Field Manual

TQM
Field Manual

James H. Saylor

McGraw-Hill, Inc.

New York St. Louis San Francisco Auckland Bogotá Caracas
Lisbon London Madrid Mexico City Milan Montreal New Delhi
Paris San Juan São Paulo Singapore Sydney Tokyo Toronto

Notices

IBM	International Business Machines, Inc.
The Juran Trilogy	Juran Institute, Inc.

FIRST EDITION
FIRST PRINTING

© 1992 by **McGraw-Hill, Inc.**

Library of Congress Cataloging-in-Publication Data

Saylor, James H.
   TQM field manual / by James H. Saylor.
     p.   cm.
   Includes index.
   ISBN 0-8306-2409-0
   1. Total quality management.   I. Title.
HD62.15.S29   1991   91-22055
658.5'62—dc20   CIP

For information about other McGraw-Hill materials, call 1-800-2-MCGRAW in the U.S. In other countries call your nearest McGraw-Hill office.

Vice President and Editorial Director: Larry S. Hager
Book Editor: Alice W. Ronke
Production: Katherine G. Brown
Book Design: Jaclyn J. Boone

To Jim, Jr., Joe, Christy, and future
generations hoping for a prosperous America

Credits

The following have granted permission to use specified materials:

Public domain information was received from the following sources:

Dell Publishing Group, Inc. for publishing *The Art of War* by Sun Tzu, edited by James Clavell.

United States Department of Commerce, National Institute of Standards and Technology for information contained in the 1991 Application Guidelines for the Malcolm Baldrige National Quality Award.

Office of Deputy Assistant Secretary of Defense for Total Quality Management OSUSD (A) TQM for many sources of information within the Department of Defense.

Boone Co. for the introductory quote from the Koito Manufacturing Company's Annual Shareholders meeting.

The following provided permissions for copyright materials:

Juran Institute, Inc. for the Joseph Juran approach to Total Quality Management contained in appendix A. Specifically, the information contained in the "The Juran Trilogy." This is a registered trademark of Juran Institute, Inc.

Massachusetts Institute of Technology, Center for Advanced Engineering Study for W. Edwards Deming's chain reaction (FIG. 1-1) and Deming's Fourteen Points (Appendix A). This information originally contained in the book *Out of Crisis*. The Fourteen Points are an updated version from the book.

Professor Theodore Levitt for the excerpts from his book *The Marketing Imagination*. They include The Total Product Concept and quote on relationships contained in chapter 4.

American Society for Quality Control Quality Press for the key elements of strategy from A. Richard Shore's book *Survival of the Fittest*. His approach is listed in Appendix A.

McGraw-Hill, Inc. for permission for information used from the following books: *Quality is Free* by Phillip Crosby, *The Improvement Process* by H. James Harrington, and *Introduction to Quality Engineering* by Genchi Taguchi.

Harper and Row Publishers, Inc. for defintion of total customer service from the book *Total Customer Service* by William H. Davidow and Bro Uttal.

Contents

Appendices

Foreword

The term Total Quality Management, or more commonly TQM, is encountered virtually every day in some form or other. Formally, TQM has come to represent the concept of everyone working together to achieve a common goal of excellence. However, there is no doubt that it is difficult to understand exactly what TQM means and how it is achieved. In researching TQM, the investigator is challenged with a great amount of information from many sources, all expounding the virtues of the concept. As is common with broad concepts and philosophies, definition and detailed application depend on the perspective of the user. This makes TQM an often misunderstood process.

I am pleased with the approach that James H. Saylor has taken in preparing the *TQM Field Manual*. His step-by-step approach—first defining the facets of TQM and then giving detailed explanations of how each segment is implemented—is extremely helpful in getting a grasp on the real issues of TQM. What I especially like about this book is the very logical layout and structure that he has established to allow its use as both a text and a desk reference.

I applaud Jim's efforts in preparing *TQM Field Manual* because it reflects his depth of understanding of the subject and his devotion to conveying the meaning of quality. From the reader's perspective it contains everything necessary to be successful in implementing a TQM program.

Finally, *TQM Field Manual* meets my two personal requirements for a valuable reference book. First, it is readable and understandable and, second and most important, the information contained in the book makes sense.

James V. Jones
President, Logistics Management Associates
Author, *Integrated Logistics Support Handbook*

Preface

This book serves as a field manual for any organization in America wishing to use the Total Quality Management (TQM) philosophy and set of guiding principles for victory in the never-ending economic war. Because all American organizations must strive for victory built from many smaller victories in the world economy of the 1990s and beyond; this book was written to satisfy customer needs and expectations for:

- A simple, easy-to-use desktop reference containing the basic TQM philosophy, guiding principles, approaches, continuous improvement systems, improvement methodologies, and tools and techniques.
- Advocation of a systematic, integrated, consistent, organization-wide approach to TQM.
- An easy-to-remember approach to TQM.
- Elimination of the notions of one best way, a quick fix, magic, or shortcut to TQM.
- Exposure of the seriousness of the economic situation.
- A book for TQM practioners, trainers, and educators.

TQM Field Manual is a desktop reference book that anyone involved in any improvement effort can use to understand the what, why, and how of TQM. Total Quality Management can benefit individuals and private and public organizations, from church groups to small businesses to local governments to the U.S. Department of Defense. Most of the well-known elements of TQM are included in this book, along with many sources of further information.

Rather than emphasize one aspect as the most important, this book looks at TQM as a total, integrated system. This consistent, organization-wide approach is advocated through the continued use of all elements within the TQM circle. Throughout all aspects of the TQM process, circles are used to emphasize the never-ending characteristic and the unity of the process. The objective of this book is to provide a total, integrated systems approach, and the key to that objective is the human element.

This book stresses the importance, in all improvement efforts, of people. When all the models, the methodology, and the tools and techniques are examined, we find that people make them work. People are the most valuable resource in any TQM effort. The people in any organization want to be treated as important resources. Most people want trust and honesty to be integral to the workplace. They need personal involvement, pride of work-manship, and ownership of their jobs. With ownership, people have the authority to take the necessary actions. Self-esteem is important. My primary message, when implementing a TQM approach, is to listen to the people. They truly know best.

The focus of this book is to provide as much information as possible about the many ways to tailor TQM to your specific situation. This book provides examples of the tailoring process with an easy-to-remember approach based on victory. In fact this book is the result of tailoring through continuous improvement of the many well-known TQM concepts. The TQM process must be tailored to your organization's concept of victory since victory is different for every organization.

In addition, the U.S. Department of Defense's approach to total quality is described as an example of the implementation of TQM by a public organization.

There is one caution regarding tailoring.

Although the approaches and the tools and techniques can be tailored to each organization, the one note of caution is never to violate the TQM philosophy or any of the guiding principles. If you pick and choose only certain parts of the TQM philosophy or guiding principles, victory will elude you. You must establish and maintain all the elemens of victory.

The war theme is used to convey the seriousness of the economic situation in the United States today. We are engaged in total economic war. Our very survival as an economic force is at stake. Already there have been many casualties. Many organizations and people have been wounded, and some have been destroyed. Such losses affect both private and public organizations and impact all aspects of our economy. Total Quality Management is the process that can turn defeat into victory. Both industry and government must use this process; America's future depends on our success in the economic war.

Finally, this book can be used as the framework for introductory Total Quality Management training and education. It provides the basic information needed by instructors and students for the application of TQM. This basic information can be tailored to the specific objectives of the organization and the needs of the students. TQM education requires the active involvement of students to ensure that they gain an understanding of the specific application of TQM. I recommend that students discover examples, reasons, approaches, and applications as part of the student participation in any TQM course. In their discovery, students find successes and failures, bad examples and good, and the most current examples. Most important, they discover for themselves that TQM applications are ever-changing, different for every organization, and must be adjusted to the organization in question. For these reasons, specific applications are not presented in this book except in the tools and techniques chapters. Each individual and organization must understand how TQM applies to it. This requires a personalization of TQM that can only come from the active search by each individual and organization for applications specific to its environment. This book offers the framework for such a personalization of TQM.

Before you begin reading this book, remember that although this field manual provides the mission, objectives, tactics, operations, and weapon systems of TQM, it is up to the organization and the individual to apply them to achieve victory.

Acknowledgments

A special acknowledgment goes to all the Aerojet Electronics Systems Division's Project 89 crew: Ellen Domb, Don Wolking, Gene Leist, Pete Weber, Dick Rawcliffe, and Mary Hickey. This book is the result of continuous improvement of their initial work.

Also, thanks are due to Aerojet Electronics Systems Division for giving me the chance to experience all aspects of the Total Quality Management efforts.

In addition, this book is the result of the efforts of many. Contributions, comments, and assistance were provided by John Bowers, Jack Duffy, Dave Ford, Brandon Hamilton, Frank Herrmann, Jeff Hill, Rosann Saylor, and Diane Solis.

Special appreciation goes to Shirley Noel-Kondek for her editorial comments and assistance in the composition of this book.

Additional thanks go to Drs. Jim Kowalick and Ellen Domb who made sure I did not go too far off the deep end.

Also my appreciation goes to Mr. Norman Michaud, past president of the Society of Logistics Engineers (SOLE), for giving me the opportunity to refine many of the concepts in this book at SOLE Total Quality Management workshops.

Further, the developers of the *Draft Department of Defense Total Quality Management Guide* deserve recognition for a job well done. It was this guide that gave me the inspiration to write the present work. In addition, thanks are due to Peter Angiola of the Office of the Under Secretary of Defense for Acquisition, Total Quality Management, for an outpouring of information on TQM in the Department of Defense.

In addition, I have used much outstanding material taken directly from the 1991 Application Guidelines for the Malcolm Baldrige National Quality Award. This application is a valuable, noncopyrighted source of quality information that is available from the U.S. Department of Commerce, National Institute of Standards and Technology, Gaithersburg, Maryland 20899.

I appreciate the cooperation of the Boone Company for the quote "You lost the economic war." This was shouted at American shareholders by Japanese shareholders in Tokyo at the Koito Manufacturing Company's annual stockholders meeting on June 29, 1990.

Finally, the assistance and patience of Rosann Saylor, my wife, during this entire process deserves recognition.

As with all worthwhile efforts today, this was truly a team effort. Each member of the team deserves special recognition for his or her specific contribution to customer satisfaction.

Introduction

America, you lost the economic war!

Annual Meeting, Koito Manufacturing—June 1990

As we enter the 1990s and look ahead to the next century, we are faced with many new challenges. The greatest of these challenges is achieving victory in a new war. This war is not a military war; it is an economic war. Victory in this economic war is just as important as victory in any military war. In fact, the impact might be even greater. Survival of the United States as an economic power is at stake.

Differences between an economic and a military war make victory difficult to achieve in the former case. First, victory cannot be clearly defined. Victory varies for each specific organization. Second, victory is forever changing. Therefore, the achievement of many, continuous victories is the goal, with the organization always striving for supreme excellence. Third, the enemy is not always obvious. The enemy can be any element that keeps an organization from achieving customer satisfaction. Enemy elements might be the competition, technology, government, or even ourselves. Fourth, the war is never-ending. Even if an organization achieves many victories, in an economic war, achievement of victory is a never-ending process.

To achieve victory in this war, an organization must learn to adapt to today's environment with an eye toward tomorrow. Currently, many approaches are available to meet this challenge. These approaches have various names, such as Total Quality Control, Total Quality Improvement, Total Improvement, Total Quality, Quality Leadership, Quality Improvement, Process Improvement, Continuous Measurable Improvement, Employee Involvement, and so on. These approaches can be considered Total Quality Management (TQM). TQM is not one specific "best" approach; rather it is a term that has evolved to encompass all efforts to achieve victory. TQM is the philosophy and set of guiding principles required by any organization striving for victory in an economic war.

This field manual is for everyone, organization or individual, who wants to strive for victory. Although victory might be different for every organization, the aim of TQM is the same for an individual, a small business, a large enterprise, a nonprofit association, and a government agency striving to achieve victory. The basic focus is the same for a service-oriented and a product-oriented organization: total customer satisfaction.

This book provides a field guide for anyone involved in the Total Quality Management process. The basic framework, along with some in-depth information, is provided to allow any organization to determine the specific elements necessary for it to achieve victory. You can read it cover to cover or study specific sections for particular information because the book can be used as a how-to manual for certain TQM methodologies. Further, it can be used as an education and training book to introduce all aspects of Total Quality Management.

This book is organized into four parts to guide you through the TQM process:

Part I   Total Quality Management overview
Part II   Making TQM work to achieve victory
Part III Improvement methodology, its tools and techniques
Part IV   The final campaign

Part I (chapters 1 through 3) discusses the basics of TQM. The background, philosophy, guiding principles, and a practical TQM model are provided. The reason TQM exists, that is, the reason changes are necessary, are presented. In addition, Part I explains what it takes to achieve victory.

Part II (chapter 4) provides a basic framework so that an individual or organization can make TQM work. This chapter focuses on the overall process of creating and maintaining a TQM environment, establishing and maintaining a continuous improvement system, and focusing on total customer satisfaction, all essential elements of TQM.

Part III (chapters 5 through 10) describes the improvement methodologies of TQM, along with specific improvement tools and techniques. These tools and techniques are grouped into four categories: people involvement, process understanding, selection analysis, and system improvement.

Part IV (chapters 11 and 12) is a discussion of the final campaign. These chapters discuss the strategy, tactics, operations, and "weapon systems" required to achieve victories in the final campaign. Special emphasis is placed on the role of total integrated logistics as a secret weapon in the economic war. Chapter 12 provides detailed information on the implementation of Total Quality Management within the U.S. Department of Defense and the defense industry. This chapter gives another model within the public sector of the implementation of Total Quality Management.

Remember, this is a war. Wage this war with the same fervor and support as you would any other war. Survival depends on it. Everyone must work toward victory.

Part I

Total Quality Management Overview

1

What Total Quality Management is

*To fight and conquer in all your battles is not supreme
excellence; supreme excellence consists in breaking the enemy's
resistance without fighting.* *

Sun Tzu
Art of War

In these times of extreme economic competition, many organizations use a Total Quality Management (TQM) approach to achieve many small victories that build into a larger victory. In the atmosphere of economic war, American industry needs a full arsenal. TQM is a philosophy and set of principles aimed at transforming an organization into one capable of achieving victories. TQM provides any organization the means for meeting the many challenges of today while ultimately moving the organization toward the future.

TQM focuses the organization on continuous improvement geared to total customer satisfaction. This customer-oriented process combines fundamental management practices with existing improvement efforts and proven tools and techniques. TQM is applicable to every organization striving for victory, whether the organization be a single function, a division, or a huge corporation. Total Quality Management is equally useful for large and small businesses, manufacturing and service industries, and public and private organizations.

---

*From *Art of War*, James Clavell, Ed., Dell Publishing, 1983.

TQM background

Total Quality Management evolved from a wide range of earlier management practices, manufacturing productivity enhancements, and improvement efforts. TQM has its roots in the "quality" movement that catapulted Japan into its current position as leading economic power in the global marketplace. The Japanese concept of quality focused on product and performance. Only later did management approaches such as TQM change the emphasis of the concept of quality to customer satisfaction.

The quality improvement movement actually originated in both the United States and Japan prior to World War II. During World War II, Americans continued to improve the concepts of manufacturing productivity improvement and after World War II, the Japanese aggressively pursued the idea of quality improvement. W. Edwards Deming, an American, helped the Japanese with their obsession with quality. Figure 1-1, from Deming's book *Out of the Crisis*, shows the Deming chain reaction, which played a major role in the Japanese's focus on quality. Simply put, quality improvement became the vision for everyone in Japan.

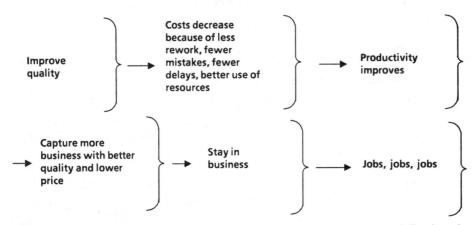

Fig. 1-1. Deming's Chain Reaction. (Courtesy MIT Center for Advanced Engineering Study)

Many others also assisted the Japanese in their pursuit of the "quality" vision during the decades after World War II. The most notable were Joseph M. Juran, Armand V. Feigenbaum, Kaoru Ishikawa, and Genichi Taguchi. Joseph M. Juran, a leading quality planning advocate and, like Deming, an American, taught the Japanese his concepts of quality planning.

In their works, both Juran and Deming stress traditional management as the root cause of quality and productivity issues. Juran focuses on a disciplined planning approach to quality improvement.

Armand V. Feigenbaum, also an American, was the first to use the term total quality. His book *Total Quality Control* was one of the best early works on total quality improvement; approaching the topic from a systematic, integrated, organization-wide perspective. Feigenbaum also originated the cost-of-quality concept, which monitored the cost of failures, quality appraisal, and failure prevention costs. This turned managers' attention toward quality improvement through the reduction of the cost of quality.

Kaoru Ishikawa, Japan's leading expert, geared the quality vision to the masses. In his program, he stressed seven basic tools of quality used for problem solving in the belief that these tools could solve almost any quality problem. These tools included the Pareto chart, cause-and-effect diagram, stratification, check sheet, histogram, scatter diagram, and Shewhart (Deming) cycle. These seven basic tools are detailed in chapters 5 and 9 and Appendix F of this book.

Genichi Taguchi, another of Japan's top experts on quality, was the first to stress proper design strategy. He redefined the concepts of design specifications. Believing that simply being within specifications was not good enough, he introduced a methodology that focuses on design optimization.

In the Taguchi approach, any variation of performance from best target values is a loss, and loss is the enemy of quality. The goal is to minimize loss by focusing on the best target value. Taguchi's approach is described in chapter 10.

During the 1950s, 1960s, and early 1970s, the United States did not feel the need to embrace the quality vision. America was the number-one economic power in the world, and the world bought the goods that the U.S. produced. However, during the late 1970s, the threat of competition from other countries became apparent to many U.S. industries. America started to investigate ways to become more competitive. As a result, a U.S.-style TQM evolved and in the process took advantage of some strengths of American culture such as heterogeneity, individuality, innovation, and creativity. As it exists today, this American-style TQM stresses a totally integrated, systematic, organization-wide approach that requires the transformation of many of the ways America traditionally does business.

In addition to the early quality experts whose teachings are still valid, many others joined the march to quality and provided further insights into the transformation process. Some of the better-known proponents of the approach include Philip B. Crosby, Tom Peters, H. James Harrington, and A. Richard Shores.

In the late 1970s, Philip B. Crosby outlined the Zero Defects system in his book *Quality is Free*. The program was instrumental in uncovering many defects in the American industrial process and was embraced by many American companies and the U.S. government. The Crosby approach is based on four points: quality is conformance to requirements; prevention is the key to quality; the Zero Defects concept is the standard; and measurement is the price of nonconformance.

In the early 1980s, Tom Peters and Robert H. Waterman, Jr., prodded American business with ideas about the ingredients that contributed to the success of the top companies in America. Their book *In Search of Excellence* presented an initial, inside look at the factors that made these companies so competitive. They determined that eight attributes distinguished excellent, innovative American companies. First, these organizations were geared for action. They preferred to do something, rather than going through endless analyses and committee reports. Second, they continuously strove to meet the needs and expectations of their customers: they learned customer preferences and they met those preferences. Third, innovative organizations were structured with smaller companies within, allowing internal autonomy and entrepreneurship and encouraging open communication, independent thinking, and competitiveness. Fourth, successful organizations fostered the ability to increase productivity through people. Central to this effort was creating an awareness in all employees that their best efforts were essential and that they would share in the company's success. Fifth, they were value driven through the application of hands-on attention by management to the organization's essential purpose. Sixth, they built on the organization's strengths by sticking to what they did best. Seventh, successful organizations had a simple form with lean staff, that is, few layers of management and few people in each layer. Eighth, excellent organizations showed simultaneous loose-tight properties. They created an atmosphere of dedication to the primary values of the company and a tolerance for all employees who accepted those values.

In 1987, Tom Peters published another book, *Thriving on Chaos*, in which he said that there was no such thing as an excellent company. He was referring to the constant changes in the new environment; a company in the new environment must continuously improve, or other companies will replace it. Therefore, a company can never achieve excellence. Peters called for a management revolution in America, a revolution that constantly adapts to the many challenges in the economic environment of today.

In the late 1980s, many other Americans updated the teachings of the earlier quality experts. For instance, H. James Harrington from IBM and A. Richard Shores from Hewlett-Packard Company provide excellent, proven road maps for Total Quality Management in American industry today. Harrington's approach is described in his book *The Improvement Process*. Shores's book *Survival of the Fittest* outlines his teachings. The Harrington approach focuses on the entire improvement process, whereas Shores's stresses total quality control. Both quality practitioners provide many specific methods geared to today's American industry.

In 1988, the Department of Defense (DoD) adopted the Total Quality Management approach. TQM was to be the vehicle for attaining continuous quality improvement within DoD and its many contractors.

In the future, Total Quality Management will be adopted by many other government agencies and private industries in America. America can procrastinate no longer.

The Total Quality Management definition

Total Quality Management (TQM) is both a philosophy and a set of guiding principles that are the foundation of a continuously improving organization. TQM is the application of quantitative methods and human resources to improve the material services supplied to an organization, all the processes within the organization, and the degree to which the needs of the customer are met, now and in the future. TQM integrates fundamental management techniques, existing improvement efforts, and technical tools under a disciplined approach focused on continuous improvement.

This definition, offered in the *Draft Department of Defense Total Quality Management Guide*, is only one of many definitions of TQM. However, this DoD definition of Total Quality Management is used as the basis of this field manual.

No one definition of TQM is accepted by everyone. The definition of TQM varies from organization to organization and individual to individual. This definition of TQM, as applied, is usually internalized by each specific organization and individual. Although the applied definitions vary, the DoD definition includes all the essential elements of TQM. The four essential elements of all definitions of TQM are continuous process improvement, people orientation, quantitative methods, and customer focus.

Further understanding of Total Quality Management comes when the terms that make up the name are defined.

Total in this context means the involvement of everyone and everything in the organization in a continuous improvement effort.

Quality is total customer satisfaction. Total customer satisfaction is the center or focus of TQM. The customer is everyone affected by the product and/or service and is defined in two ways. The customer is the ultimate user of the product and/or service—known as an external customer—and the customer is the next process in the organization—known as an internal customer. TQM focuses on satisfying all customers, internal and external.

Management is the leadership of an organization. Management creates and maintains the TQM environment.

The Total Quality Management philosophy

The Total Quality Management philosophy provides the overall concepts that foster continuous improvement in an organization. This philosophy stresses a systematic, integrated, consistent, organization-wide perspective involving everyone and everything. It focuses primary emphasis on total satisfaction for both the internal and external customer, within a management environment that seeks continuous improvement of all systems and processes. The TQM philosophy emphasizes the use of all people, usually in multifunctional teams, to bring about improvement from within the organization. It stresses optimal life cycle cost and uses measurement within a disciplined methodology to target improvements. The prevention of defects and an emphasis on quality in design are key elements of the philosophy. The elimination of losses and reduction of variability are important aims. Further, it advocates the development of relationships—employee, supplier, and customer. Finally, the philosophy is based on an intense desire to achieve victory.

TQM guiding principles

The TQM guiding principles are the fundamental rules required to achieve victories. These principles involve continuously performing the following actions:

Provide a TQM environment.
Reward and recognize appropriate actions.
Involve everyone and everything.
Nurture supplier partnerships and customer relationships.
Create and maintain a continuous improvement system.
Include quality as an element of design.
Provide training and education.
Lead long-term improvement efforts for error prevention.
Encourage cooperation and teamwork.
Satisfy the customer, both internal and external.

The TQM umbrella

The TQM umbrella includes the integration of all of the fundamental management techniques, existing improvement efforts, and technical tools used under a disciplined approach that is focused on continuous improvement. Figure 1-2 shows some of the current best-known improvement efforts. These efforts include concurrent engineering (CE), robust design (RD), statistical process control (SPC), just-in-time (JIT), cost of quality (COQ), total production maintenance (TPM), manufacturing resource planning (MRPII), computer-aided design (CAD), computer-aided engineering (CAE), computer-aided manufacturing (CAM), computer integrated manufacturing (CIM), information systems (IS), total integrated logistics (TIL), design of experiments (DOE), and total customer service (TCS). These improvement efforts are described in later chapters of this book.

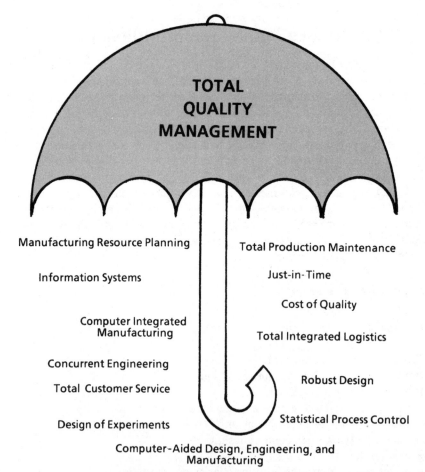

Fig. 1-2. The TQM umbrella covers many improvement efforts.

All of the improvement efforts are geared toward the improvement of one or more aspects of an organization. For instance, robust design, statistical process control, just-in-time, cost of quality, total production maintenance, manufacturing resource planning, computer-aided design, computer-aided engineering, computer-aided manufacturing, and computer integrated manufacturing are engineering and manufacturing oriented. These existing improvement efforts can show some visible results by themselves. However, TQM integrates all of these improvement efforts to enhance the overall effectiveness of the entire organization, focusing on customer satisfaction.

A comparison: traditional management versus TQM

To get a clearer understanding of what TQM is, TABLE 1-1 provides some comparisons between traditional management and Total Quality Management.

Table 1-1. Traditional management and TQM comparison.

Traditional Management	Total Quality Management
Looks for "quick fix"	Adopts a new management philosophy
Fire-fights	Uses structured, disciplined operating methodology
Operates the same old way	Advocates breakthrough thinking using small innovations
Randomly adopts improvement efforts	"Sets the example" through leadership
Focuses on short term	Stresses long-term, continuous improvement
Inspects for errors	Prevents errors and emphasizes quality of design
Decides using opinions	Decides using facts
Throws resources at a task	Uses people as primary means to add value
Is motivated by profit	Focuses on customer satisfaction
Relies on programs	Is a new way of life

TQM is a people-oriented, measurement-driven, customer-focused management philosophy using a structured, disciplined operating methodology. It is not a quick fix that uses fire-fighting techniques. TQM uses many small, continuous improvements and innovations, rather than simply operating the same old way, with business as usual.

With TQM, management must set the example by leading the long-term continuous improvement effort. In the past, organizations often adopted improvement efforts randomly and for a short period only.

TQM focuses on "doing the right thing right the first time." This approach prevents errors and emphasizes quality of design. Traditionally, inspection has been the method used to find and eliminate errors.

Further, TQM bases decisions on fact, not opinions, as traditional management often does.

TQM's use of people's capabilities as a primary means of adding value to a product or service is also a major variation from the traditional approach. In the past, management tended to increase resources or technology to add value to its product or service.

Above all, the TQM philosophy focuses on customer satisfaction. It is not solely motivated by profit.

Finally, TQM is not simply a new management program; it is a new way of life.

The Total Quality Management process

Total Quality Management focuses on the continuous improvement of all systems and processes in an organization. In fact, TQM is a process itself, a process within the overall system of the organization. The entire organization is a system made up of many processes to accomplish the functions of the organization—one of which is TQM.

What is a process? A process is a series of activities that takes an input, modifies the input, and produces an output.

The TQM process transforms all the inputs in the organization into a product and/or service that satisfies the customer. In FIG. 1-3, the overall TQM process consists of the inputs received from a supplier, the process itself, and the outputs supplied to the customer. A process has many inputs, including manpower, material, methods, machines, and the external environment, but the most important inputs include the wants, desires, needs, expectations, and requirements of the customer. The output of the process is a satisfied customer.

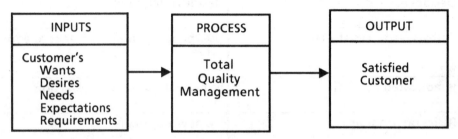

Fig. 1-3. The Total Quality Management process.

The Victory-C TQM model

The Victory-C Total Quality Management model is shown in the circle in FIG. 1-4. The letter C stands for customer. The model is enclosed in a circle to indicate the total, integrated, systematic nature of TQM.

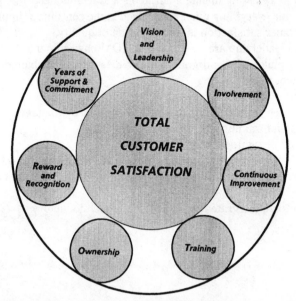

Fig. 1-4. The Victory-C Total Quality Management model.

All the elements required to achieve victory are included inside the circle. The center, or focus, is the customer and his satisfaction; the major target of TQM is total customer satisfaction. The requirements for victory are:

Vision and leadership
Involvement of everyone and everything
Continuous improvement of all systems and processes
Training and education
Ownership, the authority to act
Reward and recognition
Years of commitment and support from management

Key points

- Total Quality Management provides a process for every organization striving to achieve victory today and in the future.
- TQM evolved from a wide range of earlier management practices, tools and techniques, manufacturing productivity enhancements, and improvement efforts.

- TQM does the following:
  - ~ Uses people's abilities to add value.
  - ~ Applies a disciplined approach stressing quantitative methods.
  - ~ Establishes continuous improvement aimed at systems and processes.
  - ~ Focuses on the customer, both internal and external.
  - ~ Integrates existing management tools and techniques.
- Everyone and everything must be involved in the continuous improvement effort.
- Total customer satisfaction is the definition of quality.
- Vision and leadership are essential in a TQM environment.
- The TQM philosophy and guiding principles require a change from traditional management practices.
- Ownership is an important element.
- TQM requires years of commitment and support by management.
- Education and training are offered continuously.
- Reward and recognition are part of the process.
- TQM is a process for transforming customer requirements, wants, and desires into a product and/or service that satisfies the customer's needs and expectations.
- TQM is a total, integrated, systematic approach to victory.

2

Why Total
Quality Management?

The art of war is of vital importance to the state. It is a
matter of life and death, a road either to safety or to ruin.
Hence under no circumstances can it be neglected.

Sun Tzu
Art of War

An economic war is as important as any other war. The current economic war must not
be ignored. Every organization must learn to adapt to a new world characterized by
rapid change, rising complexity, and rabid competition. Political, technological, social,
and economic changes are the norm. With the advent of the information age, new technologies are introduced in increasing numbers. This causes rising complexities in the
processes used to perform work. Competition on a global scale is a fact of life: everyone
is competing for the new global markets. With competition fierce in all aspects—technology, cost, product quality, and service quality—everyone must seek a competitive
advantage. TQM is the proven approach needed to confront the challenges of this economic war and build victories upon victories today and in the future.

Today's world

Today's economic world is radically different from that of the recent past. In the new
environment where old solutions no longer work, America finds itself no longer in a
safe position as the world's top economic power. Many organizations have discovered
that old solutions no longer bring about expected results. America must act to regain
and maintain its prominent position as an economic power.

Some of the major differences between yesterday and today are shown in TABLE 2-1. These differences require—no, demand—that America change.

United States thinking must be changed to reflect our new stance as one of many players in the competitive global economy. Continuing to do what America has always done is no longer good enough. America must start working smarter.

Table 2-1. Comparison of yesterday's and today's worlds.

Yesterday's World	Today's World
U.S., the top economic power	U.S. one of the players
Make it, it sells	Intense competition
Quality and reliability not important	Quality and reliability demanded
Historically reasonable cost	Lowest possible cost
Many organizational layers	Few organizational layers
Rigid structures	Flexible structures
Large budgets	Shrinking budgets
New systems	Improvement of old systems
If not broke, do not fix it	Continuous improvement
Large breakthroughs	Little innovations
Development	Innovation
Sequential design	Concurrent design
Inspection	Prevention of defects
Certainty	Uncertainty
Stable technology	Rapidly changing technology
Waste: many resources	Conservation : limited resources
Compete	Cooperate
Individual	Groups
People specialized/eliminated	People flexible, primary means to add value
Strong management	Strong leadership
Leadership only at the top	Leadership at all levels

In today's global economic environment, quality and reliability are necessities. The nature and type of organizations must be transformed into flexible entities geared to superior quality, high service, and low life cycle cost. This requires turning organizations upside down and rethinking their structuring.

The current shrinking budgets of most organizations cause a reexamination of priorities and stress more than ever "more for the buck." This necessitates the improvement of old systems, rather than acquiring totally new systems. Continuous improvement through innovation is the new wave. Innovation, rather than new development, is stressed in today's world. Concurrent engineering is the present approach to providing responsive product and process design. The prevention of defects is today's focus.

To adapt to uncertainty, changing technology, and limited resources, still more changes are needed. American organizations must be flexible. They must conserve resources, learn to cooperate, work in groups, and use people and their ideas as the primary means of adding value to products and services. In addition, the emphasis must change from strong management at the top to leadership at all levels in the organization. Thus, many changes within America's industry and government are required to survive in today's economic world.

Tomorrow's world

No one can predict tomorrow's economic world, but one thing is certain: it will be different from today's. In order to make the necessary adaptations to today's economic world with an eye to the future, organizations must make continuous improvements now while focusing on the long-term environment. This change in emphasis requires a flexible organization totally responsive to the customer.

Although a completely accurate prediction of the most important forces in tomorrow's world is not possible, certain forces seem likely to predominate. These forces are economic pressures, global competition, people issues, and ever-advancing technology.

Economic pressures will continue to dominate choices and decisions in public and private organizations. The demand for increasing value at a lower cost will continue into the next century.

Global competition will no doubt increase among all nations. The competition for world markets and scarce natural resources will govern the new world order.

People issues will undoubtedly escalate in the coming years. Labor markets, especially in the United States, will shrink at the same time the demand for people with specific education and skills increases. In addition, the demand for quality of work life for all people will influence the future work environment.

Technology will continue to grow at an astounding pace. The impact of new technology, especially in information processing and communications, could determine supremacy.

Total Quality Management provides a flexible, responsive management approach able to act or to react to all of the forces of today's and tomorrow's economic world. TQM is the only known approach that focuses the resources of an organization on identifying and acting on the internal and external forces that will influence the world of tomorrow. TQM gears an organization toward continually improving quality, increasing productivity, and reducing costs to ease economic pressures. It focuses on total customer satisfaction through highest product and service quality at lowest life cycle costs to compete in the global environment. TQM stresses constant training and education, downsizing and decentralizing organizations, and using people's capabilities to add product and service value. Along with maximization of the human impact, Total Quality Management advocates the optimum use of technology to achieve a competitive advantage.

It works

Total Quality Management has transformed some nations that compete with America into economic powers. Likewise, many U.S. institutions are using TQM to pursue victory. In industry, for example, many organizations have used TQM to increase customer satisfaction. Also, TQM is at work within the U.S. Department of Defense (DoD), helping to achieve the goal stated in the *Draft Department of Defense Total Quality Management Guide* of a "satisfied, quality-equipped, quality-supported soldier, sailor, airman and Marine." The DoD reports success using TQM not only with its own organizations, but also with DoD contractors.

Examples of the success of TQM abound. Seminars, symposia, books, magazines, newspapers, newsletters, and other media provide a never-ending flow of success stories. Most organizations freely share information about TQM and extol its virtues. These stories show that TQM works in both the private and public sectors. The Malcolm Baldrige National Quality Award winners provide excellent examples of success stories in the United States. Some past award winners include Motorola, Inc.; Federal Express; Westinghouse Electric Corporation's Commercial Nuclear Fuel Division; Globe Metallurgical, Inc.; IBM's Rochester, Minnesota, plant; Milliken and Company; Xerox Business Products and Systems; Wallace Company, Inc.; and Cadillac Motor Car Company. In addition to these award winners, many other companies in the private sector are achieving success as a result of their TQM efforts.

Many agencies in the public sector also have success stories to tell. One of the best known is the public utility company Florida Power and Light. In 1989, it became the first company outside of Japan to win the Deming Prize. This cherished award is Japan's outstanding quality achievement award. Florida Power and Light's focus on continuous quality improvement through a TQM approach has significantly improved customer satisfaction.

TQM at work: 1990 Malcolm Baldrige Award winners

The 1990 Malcolm Baldrige National Quality Award winners provide excellent current examples of TQM success. The award-winning organizations were determined to be the "best of the best" in America in 1990. These examples given below are taken directly from the 1991 Application Guidelines (Appendix B lists the criteria). The effect of Total Quality Management is evident in every one of these outstanding organizations.

Cadillac Motor Car Company   During the 1980s, able foreign and domestic competitors gained market share at Cadillac's expense. By effectively integrating quality into all endeavors—from product planning to personnel practices—Cadillac has reversed its decline in market share, attracting new buyers while boasting the highest percentage of repeat buyers in the car industry. Its partnerships with the United Auto Workers have been a catalyst in this transformation. Cadillac employs about 10,000 people at its Detroit area headquarters, four Michigan-based manufacturing plants, and 10 sales and service zone offices in the United States.

Cadillac's turnaround began in 1985 with implementation of simultaneous engineering, the first of several major changes designed to ensure that the division's products and services would be first to meet or exceed expectations of potential buyers. More than 700 employees and supplier representatives now participate on SE teams responsible for defining, engineering, marketing, and continuously improving all Cadillac products. Alongside customers and employees, suppliers and dealers are fully integrated into Cadillac customer-focused, quality improvement efforts. Three-fourths of the division's 55 Product Development and Improvement Teams have suppliers as members. External suppliers must demonstrate continuous improvement in meeting "targets for excellence" in five key areas: quality, cost, delivery, technology, and management. Virtually all measures of performance indicate continuous quality improvement and is paying off for Cadillac.

Did Cadillac use any of the TQM concepts? Oh, yes, it did. It:

- Integrated quality into all endeavors.
- Created partnerships with the United Auto Workers.
- Practiced simultaneous engineering.
- Met or exceeded expectations of potential buyers.
- Had both employees and supplier representatives participate on SE teams.
- Aimed at continuously improving.
- Fully integrated customers and employees, suppliers and dealers.
- Practiced customer-focused, quality improvement efforts.
- Added suppliers as members of Product Development and Improvement Teams.
- Demanded suppliers demonstrate continuous improvement.
- Targeted five key areas for excellence.
- Implemented measures of performance.
- Focused on continuous quality improvement.

IBM Rochester   The concept of quality at IBM Rochester is linked directly to the customer. Detailed features are crafted from analysis of needs and expectations of existing and potential owners of computer hardware and software manufactured by IBM Rochester. Customers are directly involved in every aspect of the product from design to delivery. Managers and nonmanagers alike have clearly defined quality improvement goals. Often working in teams that erase departmental boundaries, they have authority to determine how best to accomplish those goals.

IBM Rochester, which employs more than 8,100 people, recently strengthened its strategic quality initiatives by formulating improvement plans based on six critical success factors: improved products and service requirements definition, enhanced product strategy, 6-0 (six-sigma) defect elimination strategy, further cycle time reductions, improved education, and increased employee involvement and ownership.

The IBM Rochester quality culture has been transformed from reliance on technology-driven processes to market-driven processes directly involving suppliers, business partners, and customers, delivering solutions. A 30-percent productivity improvement

occurred between 1986 and 1989. Product-development time for new, midrange computer systems has been reduced by more than half, while the manufacturing cycle has
been trimmed 60 percent since 1983. Customers benefited from a threefold increase in
product reliability and a reduced cost. IBM Rochester's share of the world market for
intermediate computers increased one full percentage point in both 1988 and 1989, and
revenue growth in 1989 was double the industry rate.

Did IBM Rochester practice the concepts of TQM? It did in many ways. It:

- Embraced the concept of quality.
- Linked quality directly to the customer.
- Performed an analysis of needs and expectations.
- Directly involved customers in every aspect of the product from design to deliv-
  ery.
- Clearly defined quality improvement goals.
- Created teams that erased departmental boundaries.
- Gave authority to teams.
- Formulated improvement plans.
- Identified critical success factors.
- Created a quality culture.
- Aimed for market-driven processes directly involving suppliers, business part-
  ners, and customers, delivering solutions.
- Benefited customers.

Federal Express Corporation   Federal Express's "People-Service-Profit"
philosophy guides management policies and actions. Employees are encouraged to
innovate and make decisions that advance quality goals. Federal Express provides
employees with the information and technology needed to improve their performance
continuously. Consistently included in the listing of best U.S. companies to work for,
Federal Express has a "no-layoff" philosophy, and its "guaranteed fair treatment procedure" for handling employee grievances is used as a model by firms in many industries.

Federal Express launched the air-express industry in the mid-1970s. The company
achieved high levels of customer satisfaction and experienced rapid sales growth.
Today, approximately 90,000 Federal Express employees, at over 1,650 sites, process
1.5 million shipments daily. Domestic overnight and second-day deliveries account for
nearly three-fourths of the total, with the remainder being international deliveries. The
firm's air cargo fleet is now the world's largest. Federal Express revenues totaled $7
billion in fiscal year 1990.

Customer satisfaction is high, but past accomplishments do not ensure future success. Through a quality improvement program focusing on 12 Service Quality Indicators (SQIs) tied to customer expectations, the Memphis-based firm sets higher
standards for service and customer satisfaction. The company has set up cross-functional teams for each service component in the SQI. Two of these corporate-wide teams
have over 1,000 employees working on improvements. Measuring themselves against a
100 percent service standard, managers and employees strive to improve all aspects of
Federal Express.

Federal Express also embraced the TQM concepts in numerous ways. It:

- Adopted a philosophy that guides management policies and actions.
- Encouraged employees to innovate and make decisions.
- Provided information and technology.
- Aimed for continuous improvement of its performance.
- Developed a no-layoff philosophy.
- Guaranteed a fair treatment procedure.
- Achieved customer satisfaction.
- Implemented a quality improvement program focusing on 12 Service Quality Indicators tied to customer expectations.
- Set higher standards.
- Set up cross-functional teams.
- Measured themselves against a 100-percent service standard.
- Encouraged managers and employees to strive to improve all aspects.

Wallace Company, Inc.   Founded in 1942, Wallace is a family-owned distribution company headquartered in Houston that primarily serves the chemical and petrochemical industries. Its 10 offices, located in Texas, Louisiana, and Alabama, distribute pipe, valves, and fittings as well as value-added specialty products such as actuated valves and plastic-lined pipe. Wallace distributes directly in the Gulf Coast area but serves international markets as well. In 1989 sales totaled $79 million. The company employs 280 associates, all of whom have been trained in quality improvement concepts and methods.

The Wallace quality initiatives have paid numerous dividends. Since 1987, Wallace's market share has increased from 10.4 percent to 18 percent. In 1985, Wallace adopted a long-term strategy of Continuous Quality Improvement. In only a few years, the company distinguished itself from its competitors by setting new standards for service. Wallace effectively merged business and quality goals, built new partnerships with customers and suppliers, and instilled associates with a commitment to one overriding aim: total customer satisfaction. Nearly everyone at Wallace is a member of a quality team.

Wallace established a Total Customer Response Network that must respond to all inquiries and complaints within 60 minutes. Its customer base has expanded. As a result, since 1987 its sales volume has grown 69 percent and, because of greater efficiency, operating profits through 1989 increased 7.4 times.

Did the Wallace Company, Inc., share the TQM philosophy? Count the ways. It:

- Trained associates in quality improvement concepts and methods.
- Adopted a long-term strategy of Continuous Quality Improvement.
- Merged business and quality goals.
- Built new partnerships with customers and suppliers.
- Instilled associates with a commitment to one overriding aim: total customer satisfaction.
- Made nearly everyone a member of a quality team.
- Established a Total Customer Response Network.

Results of TQM

Many specific results can be attributed to TQM efforts, some of which have been cited in the previous paragraphs. Of course, the major result is customer satisfaction. This can further result in achieving a specific victory for an organization. Victory for different organizations might be defined by a variety of terms, such as survival; more capital; increased stockholder earnings; larger market share; more jobs; competitive advantage; higher profits; or an increased quality of life, exceptional service, and benefits.

Specifically, some of the other benefits of TQM include:

- More profit
- Decreased cost
- Less waste
- Reduced cycle time
- No defects
- Fewer problems
- Reduced inventory
- Increased productivity
- Improved reliability
- Greater sales
- Superior product quality
- Higher employee morale
- Exceptional service quality
- Quicker response to customers
- Reduced development time
- Better quality of life for employees
- More jobs
- Increased return on investment

Some specific results reported by American organizations are well worth a closer look. Did the Malcolm Baldrige Award winners gain results? Details indicate they did.

Results of the Cadillac Motor Car Company

- Reversed its decline in market share
- Attracted new buyers while boasting the highest percentage of repeat buyers in the car industry

Results of IBM Rochester

- Improved productivity by 30 percent
- Reduced product development time by more than half
- Trimmed the manufacturing cycle by 60 percent
- Increased product reliability threefold
- Reduced cost
- Increased share of the world market for intermediate computers by 1 percent.
- Doubled the industry rate for revenue growth

Results of the Federal Express Corporation

- Became a model for grievance procedures to other firms
- Achieved high levels of customer satisfaction
- Experienced rapid sales growth
- Became world's largest air cargo fleet
- Totaled $7 billion in revenues

Results of the Wallace Company, Inc.

- Increased market share from 10.4 to 18 percent.
- Distinguished the company from its competitors by setting new standards for service
- Responded to all inquiries and complaints within 60 minutes.
- Expanded its customer base.
- Increased its sales volume by 69 percent.
- Increased operating profits 7.4 times.

Key points

- America is engaged in an economic war. This war cannot be neglected. Our survival as an economic power is at stake.
- Today's world is radically different from that of the recent past.
- Change is necessary to survive in today's economic world and to strive for victory in the future.
- Tomorrow's economic world will require more changes.
- Total Quality Management provides the process necessary to make the required changes in America for the future.
- Total Quality Management produces results.

Part II

Making TQM
Work to
Achieve Victory

3

What it takes
to achieve victory

*The general who hearkens to my counsel and acts upon it will
conquer—let such a one be retained in command! The general who
hearkens not to my counsel nor acts upon it will suffer defeat—
let such a one be dismissed! But remember: While heeding the
profit of my counsel, avail yourself also of any helpful
circumstances over and beyond the ordinary rules and modify your
plans accordingly.*

Sun Tzu
Art of War

Total Quality Management requires the creation and maintenance of a TQM environment focused on total customer satisfaction in order for an organization to achieve victory.

There are many road maps to victory. All the roads must be examined to find the best path for each specific organization. There can be no quick fix, no shortcuts, and no magic formula. TQM requires many years of dedicated, hard work.

Although many roads lead to victory, most organizations develop their own path based on the many proven paths. It is important for each organization to select a proven path that will get to its desired destination.

This book provides a practical synthesis of many of the experts' approaches that can be adapted to any organization for victory.

The TQM environment

A TQM environment must be established and maintained over the long term. This environment requires a systematic, integrated, consistent, organization-wide perspective. It does not just happen. The TQM environment must include the entire organization and must be shared by everyone in the organization. This requires the creation of an environment focused on total customer satisfaction that fosters the attainment of victory. This is the Victory-C model, shown in FIG. 1-4 in chapter 1. All of the elements of Victory-C are absolutely essential for survival today and for victories in the future. This TQM environment starts with top leadership and key people throughout the organization.

TQM must be manifested in every aspect of the organization. First, a vision must be developed and stated by top leadership. The vision is the purpose of the organization and must be shared by everyone in the organization. In addition to a vision, the environment must be developed by leadership and maintained throughout the organization. Equally essential are the involvement of everyone and everything and the continuous improvement of all systems and processes. A fourth necessity is a program of training and education that must be constantly provided. Fifth, ownership and responsibility for all systems and processes must be established and fostered. Sixth, rewards and recognitions must be systematized to reinforce desired behavior. And seventh, management must provide years of personal commitment and support to ensure victory. Finally, all of the essential elements must be focused on total customer satisfaction. These elements, which make up the TQM environment, are explained in the following sections of this chapter.

Vision and leadership

A vision must be developed by top management to indicate where the organization wants to go. The vision is what the organization sees as victory. Since victory varies from organization to organization, each will have its own vision. Although top management must create the vision, it must be shared by everyone in the organization. In addition, it must transcend the organization. This is accomplished by communication and example. The organization must continually communicate the vision through all means possible and repeatedly reinforce it during all group gatherings. Information systems, newsletters, periodicals, and other organizational media must report the status of the vision. Further and most important, the vision must be communicated by action. Management must set the example through leadership. The TQM philosophy and guiding principles can be instituted in the organization only by the actions of management.

Leadership is essential in making the vision a reality. Although leaders set the example and continue to make decisions, they are not expected to have all the answers; they simply guide the organization toward the vision. In fact they must convey the importance of the individual in the organization and role of each contributor in making the vision a reality. This type of leadership is required throughout all levels of the organization. A leader may provide the guidance, means, and encouragement to perform the necessary process, but it is the individual in the organization who makes it happen.

Involvement of everyone and everything

The TQM environment requires the total involvement of the entire organization, including management, all the people in the organization, the suppliers, and the cus-

tomers, dedicated to the ultimate goal of customer satisfaction. Figure 3-1 shows everyone and everything that is included in the TQM environment.

Management   Management through leadership ensures that the total organization is geared to total customer satisfaction. Management must provide an environment
in which people can perform to the best of their abilities. This involves providing everyone the means for doing their specific process. In addition, management fosters the
development of a sense of pride and ownership of, or responsibility for, processes.
Cooperation and teamwork play important roles in the success of an organization.

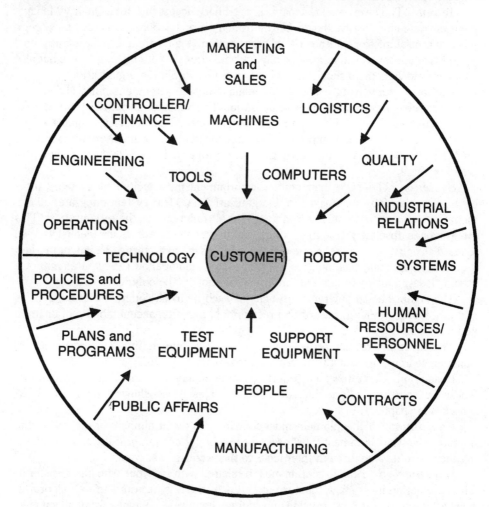

Fig. 3-1. Involvement of everyone and everything.

People in the organization   All the people in the organization must be
empowered to perform their work with excellence. In a TQM environment, people are
the most important resource. Therefore, people must be encouraged to be creative and
innovative within all areas of their work. They must be allowed to make whatever

changes are necessary within regulatory guidelines to perform the work and improve the system.

Suppliers and customers Suppliers and customers are also important players in the TQM environment. Both suppliers and customers must be integrated into the TQM process. Suppliers must understand the requirements of the organization, and the organization must weave the customer's needs and expectations into all its processes. Further, the organization must develop a continuing relationship with its suppliers and customers to ensure long-term customer satisfaction.

Teams The involvement of teams is critical to success in a Total Quality Management environment. Teams should be the primary organizational structure for accomplishing crucial missions of the critical organization. Teams are internal organizational groups that are functional and especially multifunctional. Not only employees but also suppliers and customers should participate in teams within the organization.

Include everything The TQM management environment must include not only everyone but everything in the organization. Everything includes all systems, processes, activities, jobs, tasks, capital, equipment, machines, vehicles, support equipment, facilities, tools, and computers. This management environment requires that the proper means be provided to perform the job. A proper balance of technology and people is essential.

Systems The TQM management environment must include all systems, processes, activities, jobs, and tasks of the organization. A TQM system integrates all elements of the organizational environment and all functions of the organization. This integration is absolutely essential. Many past improvement efforts erroneously stayed focused on only one area of the organization, such as manufacturing, design, or marketing. In addition, many past policies and procedures did not allow the required improvements. Today, a totally integrated improvement effort is the only way to victory.

The organizational environment includes such items as communications, policies and procedures, training, reward and recognition, benefits, accountability, evaluation, and marketing.

The functions of the organization encompass engineering, customer service, human resources, manufacturing, finance, information systems, and logistics.

In addition, all improvement efforts become elements of the TQM environment. These improvement efforts include items such as those shown under the TQM umbrella in chapter 1, FIG. 1-2.

Equipment All equipment must contribute to the attainment of the goal of the organization. The equipment must assist people in performing processes, while allowing them to add value through their ideas to the product or service.

Information All information must be shared with everyone who has a use for it. The information must show the current status of the organization, as well as projections for the future. It must provide an accurate, comprehensive picture of all supplier requirements, internal process performance, and satisfaction of customer needs and expectations.

Information sharing is critical because it shows management's commitment to victory. Management must open up all information channels. It sometimes helps for management to translate traditional management information into an easily understood form so that everyone knows what they need to do.

Critical performance information must be prominently displayed to all people who need it. This type of information should be on charts that can be easily read and updated. When possible, performance feedback should be constant and immediate. This includes all critical performance in an organization. Performance feedback is essential to the TQM environment.

Continuous improvement

The continuous improvement of all systems and processes in an organization is essential. A continuous improvement system gears the organization toward attainment of the vision. This requires the establishment and maintenance of a disciplined system for that purpose. The discipline to use this system day after day is absolutely necessary for any organization. This disciplined system must be based on trust, with everyone in the organization striving to improve the system.

The continuous improvement system applies all the fundamental aspects of the TQM definition. First, people are not the problem; they are the solution. Almost all root causes of problems in an organization or variation in a process can be traced to the system or process itself. Therefore, the continuous improvement system uses people to focus on the system, process, issue, or problem; it does not look for fault in the people.

Second, quantitative methods are the principal means for making decisions. Measurement is basic to all TQM activities in the entire organization.

Third, the continuous improvement system is the methodology for improving all material services supplied to an organization, all the processes within the organization, and the degree to which the needs of the customer are met, now and in the future.

Training and education

The organization must institute a training and an education system. Training and education are never ending for everyone in the organization. This process is an investment that must be made. Training and education provide the necessary skills and knowledge—the ability to make it happen.

Training is geared toward developing and improving specific knowledge and skills. The TQM environment requires that everyone gain additional capabilities to improve the process and perform the work. This requires TQM and job skills training. Training in TQM philosophy, guiding principles, and tools and techniques is never ending. Personal and team interaction skills must be continually refined. Specific job skills training must be provided and constantly updated to reflect the improved processes. All training must be geared to specific, clearly defined objectives; it must be performed as close as possible to the time it is required; and it must be reinforced to ensure the results needed to achieve victory.

Each organization must provide the opportunity for individual growth through education. The education system must support the goals of the organization and the individual. In addition, each individual in the organization should be encouraged to pursue a life long educational process to foster future victories for the organization and the individual.

Ownership

Ownership is important to ensure pride of workmanship. Everyone must have owner-ship of his or her work. Ownership implies responsibility, authority, and empowerment. That is, people must assume responsibility for work performance. On the other hand, they must have the authority to take the necessary actions; they must be empowered to do whatever is necessary to do the job and improve the system. This includes everyone in the organization, top leadership and all workers.

Team ownership is equally important in a TQM environment. If everyone and every team owns their work, the entire organization can work with pride toward satisfying the customer.

Reward and recognition

Reward and recognition must be instituted to support the TQM environment. Although reward and recognition are elements of any organization, the TQM environment requires a change in the usual reward and recognition systems. A reward is given for the performance of some specified action. Rewards include compensation, promotion, and benefits. Recognition is given for special or additional efforts. Recognition takes the form of a celebration. A celebration can be for an individual or group.

The reward and recognition systems of the organization must foster the TQM phi-losophy and guiding principles. They must constantly and immediately reinforce lead-ership, teamwork, individual contributions, continuous improvements, and customer satisfaction behavior.

Because the TQM environment requires that people take on new responsibilities, the reward systems must recognize this with new rewards. Any new reward system must be equitable and just. Further, it should include an appropriate combination of extrinsic and intrinsic rewards. Extrinsic rewards are those rewards given by other peo-ple and include such items as pay, promotion, and compliments. Intrinsic rewards are rewards that are an integral part of the system. These rewards come from within each individual person. Intrinsic rewards can include some of the following: a feeling of accomplishment, personal growth, improved self-esteem, a sense of belonging, and a feeling of importance. The TQM environment itself can provide many intrinsic rewards.

Years of commitment and support from management

Management must commit to long-term support. Management must be willing to invest personal time and the organization's resources, with the understanding that although some results will be quickly realized, permanent changes will take many years. This involves setting an example by displaying the expected behaviors day after day. It also includes providing the organization with a support system. This support system must provide direction, guidance, and resources for the overall TQM effort. Management must be an active, highly visible participant in all aspects of the TQM process.

Leadership must also make the commitment to total customer satisfaction as the primary focus of the organization. Total customer satisfaction must take precedence over all other influences, including cost and schedule. Because discipline is necessary to make this long-term commitment for the future victories of the organization, leadership must thoroughly understand the TQM philosophy and guiding principles must be constantly and consistently applied throughout the organization, requiring another commitment by leadership to devote personal attention to their implementation.

Focus on the customer

All the elements of victory focus on total customer satisfaction. Total customer satisfaction is the focus of the entire TQM process. Total customer satisfaction is the definition of quality. This includes all elements required to satisfy the target customer or customers, both internal and external to the organization. These elements include such items as product quality, service quality, performance, availability, durability, aesthetics, reliability, maintainability, logistics, supportability, customer service, training, delivery, billing, shipping, receiving, repairing, marketing, warranty, and life cycle cost.

TQM focuses on the customer satisfaction of both internal and external customers. Figure 3-2 shows the relationships between internal and external customers. Each proc-

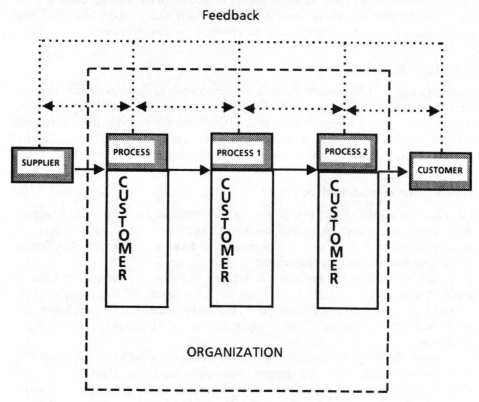

Fig. 3-2. Customer relationships.

ess in the organization is the customer of the preceding process. These are the internal customers. If each internal customer satisfies the next internal customer while focusing on external customer satisfaction, the ultimate customer—the external customer—will be satisified.

Road maps for victory

Each organization must determine its specific road map for victory. Many experts are available to help guide an organization to its destination, but most of them focus only on certain aspects of TQM. For instance, the quality consultants provide various approaches to the achievement of quality. Other experts give advice on ways to change the organizational environment. Still others give guidance on teamwork, leadership, improvement processes, manufacturing resource planning, concurrent engineering, statistical process control, and so on. Further, many organizations assist in implementation and training.

When embarking on the TQM road, an organization must use a disciplined, systematic, integrated, consistent organization-wide approach to determine the specific road map for victory. Most improvement efforts are derived from a combination of many sources. Therefore, understand as much as possible about the various options. An approach can be adopted "as is," modified, or created. Whichever approach is used, the entire organization must embrace it. If the approach is understood, advocated, supported, and owned by the organization, the chances of victory increase.

Are you ready?

Before starting a TQM process, management must analyze the organization to determine the specific TQM requirements. The check sheet in FIG. 3-3 will help determine the readiness of your organization to begin TQM implementation activities. In addition, this check sheet provides an insight into what is required to implement TQM in your specific organization. This will give the impetus to get started toward victory.

Which approach should you use?

Many approaches can be used to implement a TQM process. Most are a combination of many approaches, geared to a specific organization's needs. Above all, the approach selected should be sufficiently consistent to be understood by everyone but flexible enough to allow continuous improvement.

A careful selection of approach will increase your chances for success. Once an approach is selected, the organization must be totally committed to its execution. As with all improvement efforts, the approach must be continually review, evaluated, and improved. However, a radical change in approach can be disastrous to future improvement efforts.

Some of the most popular improvement approaches are outlined in appendix A. There are many others that also emphasize the many aspects of TQM. Your specific approach should represent a total, systematic, integrated, consistent, organization-wide perspective focused on your specific requirements for victory.

ITEM	YES	NO
Is change necessary in the organization?		
Do top management and the majority of people in the organization understand that change is necessary?		
Is there a sense of urgency for creating the required changes?		
Does the organization operate in accordance with the highest ethical standards?		
Does top management have a vision of where the organization should go? (Vision)		
Are there sufficient champions in the organization to install the TQM process? (Leadership)		
Is management willing to mobilize everyone and everything? (Involvement)		
Can an appropriate continuous improvement system be established? (Continuous Improvement)		
Is management determined to provide appropriate training? (Training)		
Can management trust the people in the organization to take ownership of work? (Ownership)		
Can appropriate reward and recognition systems be installed to foster expected behavior? (Reward)		
Is management ready to commit to years of support, funding, and resources for the TQM effort? (Years)		

Fig. 3-3. TQM readiness check sheet.

Key points

- To achieve victory requires a TQM environment focused on total customer satisfaction.

- Total Quality Management requires vision and leadership, the involvement of everyone and everything, a continuous improvement system, training and education, ownership, reward and recognition, and years of commitment and support, all focusing on total customer satisfaction.
- Total customer satisfaction is the primary aim of the TQM process.
- To be successful, Total Quality Management requires a sense of purpose, the total use of all resources, and a focused effort.
- Each organization must select its own systematic, integrated, consistent, organization-wide approach for victory.
- An organization must determine its state of readiness and analyze all the different approaches to the development of the TQM specifications for that organization.
- The approach must be embraced by the organization. To be successful, the pursuit of victory must become the primary obsession of everyone in the organization.

4

How to achieve
victory

Without harmony in the state, no military expedition can be undertaken:
without harmony in the army, no battle array can be formed.

Sun Tzu
Art of War

Total Quality Management requires the creation and maintenance of a TQM environment with a continuous improvement system focused on total customer satisfaction. In
addition, a foundation of basic business ethics must underline all TQM efforts. Integrity, trust, respect, and fairness must never be violated. Further, everyone in an organization must continually foster an unswaying focus, open communication channels, and
a strong sense of belonging.

Creating and maintaining the TQM environment requires a systematic, integrated,
consistent, organization-wide approach. It requires a lot of hard work, starting at the
top of the organization and going through the entire organization. The organization
must be turned inside out, examined, and changed as appropriate for victory in its specific economic environment. This cannot be accomplished overnight. It must be created through many small, continuous successes over time.

Each organization must determine the specific changes necessary to create and
maintain the TQM environment to achieve victory. Within each organization, a distinct
operating environment exists. This operating environment has a great impact on the
performance of the organization. The changes necessary might include a new reward
system; additional members; a different organizational culture; new management or
leadership; involvement of more employees in decision making; more ethical behavior;
development of supplier partnerships; establishment of customer relationships;
increased integration of functions; a modification of the organizational structure; devel-

opment of trust among employees, suppliers, and customers; establishment of a sense of belonging; development of discipline or self-discipline; installation of measurements; creation of a new organizational way of life; and so on.

The TQM environment is created and maintained through action planning, training, and a support system. Action planning provides the vehicle for focused action. The support system guides the organization toward victory. Training gives the skills to accomplish the actions. Action planning, training, and support must be totally integrated into the everyday life of the organization.

Action planning

The first step in creating and maintaining a TQM environment is to develop a systematic, integrated, consistent, organization-wide approach. This is accomplished through action planning. Action planning differs from traditional planning in that it is a living plan for focusing the organization's actions.

Before we describe action planning, the planning process must be understood. The top portion of FIG. 4-1 provides an overview of typical planning flow. Planning is both top down and bottom up and involves only certain people at each level. The process starts with top management defining the objectives. Next, top management and middle management determine the specific goals to support the objectives. Then, middle management develops a strategy to meet the objectives and goals. Finally, middle management and all other employees determine and perform the tactics and operations necessary to make it all work.

Action planning is shown in the bottom portion of FIG. 4-1. Everyone is part of the process. With action planning, top leadership still determines the vision and objectives, but the entire organization is involved. The objectives, goals, tactics, and operations are integrated into the organization's way of life. Each phase of the planning determines specific actions. These specific actions are continually measured, reviewed, and updated by all employees in the organization. This involves constant attention by leadership and all employees to ensure that the actions are focused and the organization is performing as desired. Action planning becomes part of the everyday method of doing business.

Strategic Total Quality Management Planning

Strategic Total Quality Management Planning (STQMP) is the overall method for creating and maintaining a TQM environment. STQMP focuses the organization's actions. Figure 4-2 shows the strategic total quality management planning cycle. This is a variation of the continuous improvement cycle, detailed later in this chapter, modified for STQMP. Phase 1 of the STQMP cycle defines the vision. Phase 2 determines strategic improvement opportunities, and phase 3 selects strategic opportunities for improvement. Phase 4 develops and maintains the TQM action plan using a disciplined methodology. This plan provides the specific road map for the organization to strive for victory. Phase 5 evaluates results. The STQMP Cycle Phase 6 indicates that the complete process is repeated in a never-ending cycle.

Typical Planning Flow

Action Planning Flow

Fig. 4-1. Typical planning flow versus action planning flow.

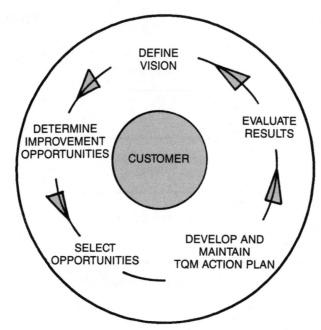

Fig. 4-2. Strategic Total Quality Management planning cycle.

The six phases of the STQMP cycle

The strategic total quality management planning cycle consists of six phases, each building on the one before:

Phase 1   Define the vision.

During this phase the organization determines its purpose or mission. This is where the organization wants to go.

Phase 2   Determine strategic improvement opportunities.

Once the organization has a purpose, the next phase is to determine the way to achieve the vision. This involves determining strategic improvement opportunities. First, the organization must determine its current situation. Second, the organization must determine the competitive environment. Third, it must identify what it must do to achieve victory over the competition.

Phase 3   Select strategic opportunities for improvement that will become the objectives of the organization.

After understanding the situation, the competition, and the improvement opportunities, choose specific strategic opportunities for improvement. These become the objectives of the organization and set the priorities throughout the organization.

Phase 4   Develop and maintain the TQM action plan using a disciplined methodology.

The goals, strategy, tactics, and operations are defined in this step. Within the strategic TQM planning cycle, a TQM action plan must be developed and maintained to provide a specific road map for the overall TQM effort and to establish a clear focus for the organization. It should be a "living" document, that is, continuously reviewed, updated, and communicated. It must be integrated into the organization's way of life. Its main purpose is to provide focused action from everyone in the organization. The plan should start with attempts to achieve little successes in a vital area. These successes should become the building blocks for creating and maintaining the TQM environment throughout the entire organization.

Phase 5 Evaluate results.

This phase measures the actions to ensure that they continue to meet the strategic objectives of the organization.

Phase 6 Do it over again in a never-ending cycle.

Continuously improve the strategic total quality management plan. It is important to build on success constantly by repeating all steps in the improvement cycle.

Steps for Total Quality Management action planning The TQM action planning steps are displayed in FIG. 4-3. A detailed description of the steps follows:

Step 1 Understand.

During this step, the organization must acquire a clear knowledge of the organizational and personal changes required to create and maintain the TQM environment. This can be accomplished through intensive interviewing, data analysis, and benchmarking. Once the changes are understood, the organization must concentrate on the specific changes required to meet its essential objectives. This means the organization must identify all the critical processes required to meet the objectives, customer needs and expectations, supplier requirements, and any problems.

Step 2 Select changes and improvement opportunities.

In this step, the organization must select the changes and improvement opportunities most likely to have an impact on the organization's objectives.

Step 3 Analyze selected changes and improvement opportunities and set goals.

An essential aspect of this step is to determine how the organization is performing. This involves the measurement of critical processes. Once the organization knows how it is performing, it can set goals for the desired improvement.

Step 4 Determine actions to meet goals.

The focus of this step is to find ways the organization can meet improve-

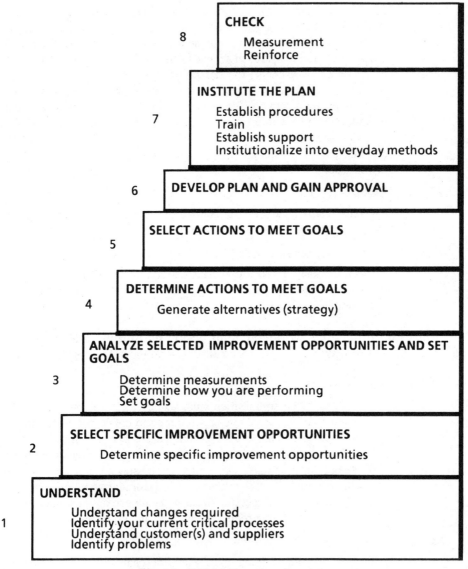

Fig. 4-3. TQM action planning steps.

ment goals. This involves identifying as many options as possible. During this step, strategy is developed and innovation and creativity are encouraged. The organization should challenge actions that have always been taken in the past. In addition, automation should be considered only after ensuring that the process is the best possible solution. Automation of an out-of-control process complicates the improvement effort.

Step 5   Select actions to meet goals.

During this step, the organization selects specific actions. This is when strategy, tactics, and operations are determined.

Step 6   Develop, maintain, and gain approval for the action plan.

This is the actual planning action step, requiring coordination and cooperation of everyone in the organization. In addition, presentations to the leadership might be appropriate to gain approval and support.

Step 7   Institute the plan.

This is the most difficult step. It requires institutionalizing the improvement by performance, procedures, training, and support.

Step 8   Check for desired results.

During this step, the improvements are continuously monitored to ensure that goals are achieved. This step requires measurements and constant communication between suppliers, owners, and customers. Owners are those in the organization who have the authority to carry out actions. Desired performance must be constantly reinforced by leadership's example.

The TQM action plan document   The TQM action plan is an on-going plan prepared with the active participation of all employees in the organization. This document becomes the basis for all actions within the organization to attain its vision and objectives. It must be readily available to everyone in the organization. Appendix C provides an outline of a model TQM action plan.

Elements of the TQM action plan   The TQM action plan must include all the essential elements for victory focused on customer satisfaction. Although each organization is different, all organizations must do the following when creating and maintaining the TQM environment:

- Determine a vision and provide leadership to make the vision a reality.
- Get everyone and everything involved in the improvement process.
- Establish a continuous improvement system.
- Provide training and education.
- Get owners involved in improvement efforts.
- Institute a reward and recognition system.
- Establish commitment and a support system.
- Focus all actions on total customer satisfaction.

Support system

A support system is critical when guiding the organization to victory. It should be integrated into the organizational structure and geared to the specific requirements of the organization. Because each organization is different, some organizations require more support than others.

In order to be effective, the support system must include the active involvement of all levels of leadership. Top leadership support is especially critical. The ultimate goal of the support system is to institutionalize the TQM process. It is important to remember that the organization must have support available to accomplish victory.

A support system can have many elements. Typically, a complete support system might include some or all of the elements shown in FIG. 4-4. These include a coach, owners, steering group, lead teams, teams, mentors, facilitators, and trainers.

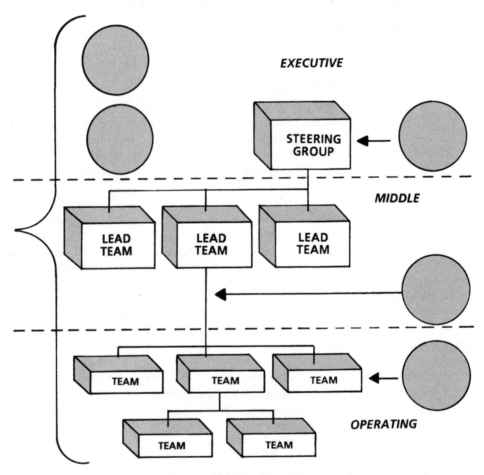

Fig. 4-4. TQM support system.

It is important to integrate the support system into the organizational structure. For instance, most likely the steering group would be the executive leadership of the organization, the lead teams would be the middle leaders of the organization, and operating teams would be everywhere in the organization.

Members of the support team

Various individuals and groups play active roles in institutionalizing the TQM process.

Coach   A coach assists the organization in creating and maintaining the TQM environment. The coach can help instruct the organization in the fundamentals of TQM, assist in orchestrating the TQM strategy, and function as the TQM overseer for the organization.

A coach is extremely useful, especially in the early stages, in helping transform the organization from a traditional management to a TQM environment. In the initial stages of creating the TQM environment, the coach might be an outside consultant. However, the consultant should work with the members of the organization to create TQM self-sufficiency within the organization. Remember, the goal is to make TQM a way of life for the organization.

Owner   An owner is a person who can change a process without further approval. Owners are at every level of the organization. An owner can be part of a team, an owner can be outside the team, or an owner can be the team. A team is the primary organizational structure for accomplishing the important missions of the organization. An owner, whose participation is critical in any improvement effort, must know how a process is performing and continuously look for ways for improvement. In some cases owners can perform or improve the process on their own; in other cases they need the assistance of others. Frequently they can receive assistance by creating teams.

Steering group   The steering group is an executive-level committee. Usually consisting of the top leaders of the organization, the steering group identifies and prioritizes critical processes for improvement. It provides overall guidance and support and allocates resources as appropriate. It decides on appropriate rewards and recognition. The steering group gives personal attention to all improvement efforts.

Lead team   A lead team oversees several other teams. Lead teams are usually the middle leaders of the organization and are established on a permanent basis to perform and improve critical processes. Normally they are the major organizational structure for performing the work. Lead teams can be functional or multifunctional and can create other teams to accomplish and/or improve a process. In such cases, the lead team provides leadership for all teams that are improving related processes.

Teams   Teams are groups of people working together toward a common goal. They are an important aspect of Total Quality Management; they perform and improve processes. Teams can be permanent, like steering groups and lead teams, or they can be temporary. Typically many teams are formed in organizations on a temporary basis, to accomplish a specific project or mission to improve a process. Other teams are relatively permanent, problem-solving organizational structures.

Some teams are functional, consisting of all members from the same function, whereas others are multifunctional, consisting of members from several functions. They can be composed of any group or combination of groups in the organization.

The performance of teams offers many advantages over individual performance. Teams provide better decisions, allow more people to participate, increase communication, and support the systematic, integrated linkage of the organization.

Facilitator   A facilitator assists a team but is not a working member of the team. The facilitator helps the team concentrate on the mission, gives on-the-job training on the use of improvement tools and techniques, explains lessons learned from other team experiences, and assists the leader with team dynamics.

Mentor   A mentor serves as management interface support for a team. The mentor serves as a mediator between traditional management and TQM and provides management assistance for a team. The mentor assists the team in obtaining required resources and reviews the team's progress on a regular basis.

Trainers Trainers provide training as necessary in TQM and job skills. Trainers can also serve as facilitators, often very successfully.

Training

Training provides the skills to accomplish actions. A comprehensive training program is necessary to create and maintain the TQM environment and must be institutionalized within the entire organization. It must be focused on the specific behaviors and skills required for work performance and TQM. People must be constantly trained to perform their work today and in the future.

In addition, specific TQM training is required to provide the particular behaviors and skills necessary to perform in a TQM environment. This training should be given only as it is needed to the people who will use it immediately. It should start with specific training for management. Once management has the skills to lead the TQM process, the rest of the organization should be trained to ensure a systematic, integrated, consistent, organization-wide effort.

The program should include training not only for specific work skills but for all aspects of TQM. A candidate list includes TQM training for:

- Action planning
- Leadership
- Awareness
- Teams
- Team leaders
- Tools and techniques
- Steering groups
- Facilitators
- Mentors
- Owners

Putting it all together

The action planning, support, and training systems work together to create and maintain the TQM environment. The organization institutionalizes these systems into its way of life and continuously monitors, analyzes, and updates them according to the changing organizational environment.

Strategic TQM planning starts the creation and maintenance of the TQM environment. Top leadership provides this type of direction for the organization, establishing focus and selecting priorities.

Next, action planning ensures that the entire organization is performing toward the same goal.

The support system directs the organization toward the goal of victory. It provides the leadership, coaching, assistance, guidance, and resources.

Training provides the skills to accomplish the necessary actions identified through action planning.

Thus strategic TQM planning, support system, and training guide the organization to victory by focusing the organization on a common purpose, giving appropriate skills, monitoring performance and progress, and redirecting inappropriate actions, while encouraging peak performances.

Continuous improvement system

The consummate leader cultivates the Moral Law and strictly adheres to method and discipline; thus it is in his power to control success.

Sun Tzu
Art of War

A disciplined continuous improvement system is required for victory. The improvement system must be used not only continuously but consistently throughout the organization. The focus must be the continuous improvement of all systems in an organization, which are interdependent processes having a common purpose.

The continuous improvement of all systems requires a continuous improvement system that is focused on process improvement. It must accomplish three objectives. First, this system must bring processes under control. Second, it must keep them under control and make them capable; that is, it must make them predicatable and keep them within limits. Finally, it must continuously improve the processes aimed toward the best target value. This involves continuously eliminating waste, simplifying processes, and solving process problems—a never-ending cycle.

Figure 4-5 shows a continuous improvement system. The same model was modified for use as the strategic TQM planning cycle. It is important to use the same continuous improvement system consistently throughout the organization. The system can be modified as needed for each specific application. In the first case, shown in FIG. 4-2, it is to form an action plan; in the second case, shown in FIG. 4-5, it is to establish a continuous improvement system.

The continuous improvement system cycle involves five stages: defining the vision/mission, determining improvement opportunities, selecting an improvement opportunity, improving by using an improvement methodology, and evaluating the results. A sixth stage can be added as a reminder: do it again and again and again. The cycle is never ending.

Stage 1 Define the vision/mission.

During this phase, the focus and priorities are determined. First the overall vision must be established, understood, and supported. Top leadership determines the vision, with input from everyone. Then everyone in the organization ascertains his or her specific mission to accomplish the overall vision.

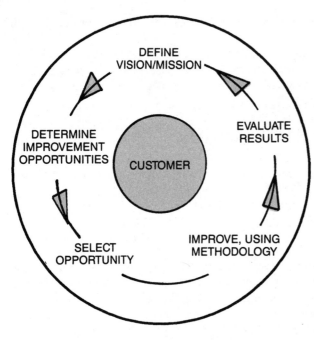

Fig. 4-5. Continuous improvement system cycle.

Stage 2   Determine improvement opportunities.

The next phase involves listing all improvement opportunities. It is important to obtain an understanding of the process at this stage. Customers, both internal and external, are identified and their needs and expectations understood. Suppliers also are matched with requirements. Any potential problems are identified at this time.

Stage 3   Select improvement opportunity.

Specific improvement opportunities are selected in this phase. Remember to focus on critical processes that have the greatest impact on customer satisfaction.

Stage 4   Improve by using the improvement methodology.

This phase uses a disciplined methodology to improve a process. This methodology is used to complete a mission, improve a process, and/or solve problems. An organization can use one of improvement methodologies. Chapter 5 describes the methodology used in this handbook. Whichever improvement methodology the organization selects, however, it should use it consistently throughout the organization.

Stage 5   Evaluate the results.

During this phase the impact of the improvements are evaluated against the overall mission/vision of the organization.

Stage 6   Do it again and again and again.

This is a never-ending process. Everyone must continuously repeat the improvement cycle.

Focus on customer satisfaction

*Hence it is only the enlightened ruler and wise general who will
use the highest intelligence of the army for the purpose of
spying, and thereby they achieve great results. Spies are a most
important element in war, because upon them depends an army's
ability to move.*

Sun Tzu
Art of War

Only customers can determine total customer satisfaction. In order to know whether
the customer is satisfied, intense observation is necessary. Only through observation,
communication—especially listening—and measurement can the organization determine total customer satisfaction. The organization must use every means available to
evaluate customer satisfaction. In chapters 5 through 10, various tools and techniques
are described to assist in determining customer satisfaction. For instance, the quality
function deployment technique described in chapter 10 is excellent for listening to the
"voice of the customer."

Customers are the focus of all Total Quality Management efforts. Without customers, the organization ceases to exist. Therefore, every organization and everyone in
the organization must constantly strive to satisfy the current customers and to create
new customers for the future.

Figure 4-6 shows what to observe to achieve total customer satisfaction. The organization must know itself, its product, its competition, and its customers.

*Fig. 4-6. Elements that must
be observed for total customer
satisfaction.*

Know yourself

Knowing yourself is an important element in achieving customer satisfaction. In the process of knowing yourself, the organization looks inward. Internal quality is the focus; total customer satisfaction is still the goal. Each customer in the organization must be satisfied. However, unlike the external customer, the internal customer might or might not be a person. The customer could be a person receiving the output of a job, or it could be the next process, the next task, the next activity, the next job, or the next piece of equipment.

To satisfy internal customers, an organization must understand, measure, and analyze all its processes to determine existing performance. Once current performance is known, goals can be set to improve the internal organization. The improvement methodology in chapter 5 and improvement tools and techniques in chapters 6 through 10 are used during this process.

Know your product

The organization must know all there is to know about its product to achieve total customer satisfaction. This includes knowing all aspects of the product. The product is an output of a process that is provided to a customer (internal/external), such as goods, services, information. The product is all aspects contributing to customer satisfaction. This can also include such items as product quality, reliability, maintainability, availability, customer service, support services, supply support, support equipment, training, delivery, billing, and marketing. Again, every one of these elements of the product and/ or service must focus on customer satisfaction. The goods or services may be the best in the marketplace, but if the product does not provide total customer satisfaction, the customer will not be satisfied and most likely will go elsewhere to find a product that does give total customer satisfaction.

Total Product Concept   The Total Product Concept from *The Marketing Imagination* by Professor Theodore Levitt of Harvard Business School provides insight into the range of possibilities for a product. In Levitt's circle in FIG. 4-7, the generic product is the basic item. The expected product, which includes the generic product, is the cus-

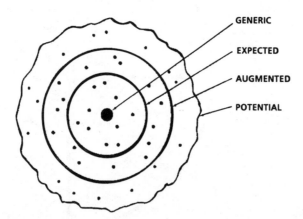

GENERIC

EXPECTED

AUGMENTED

POTENTIAL

Fig. 4-7. Total Product Concept. (Courtesy Professor Theodore Levitt)

tomer's minimal expectations. The augmented product offers more than the customer has become accustomed to expect. A potential product is anything that can be used to attract and hold customers beyond the augmented product. The Total Product Concept is important when targeting the product and/or service required to achieve customer satisfaction.

Differentiating the product   When total customer satisfaction is the goal, the product and/or service must, at a minimum, be comparable to the product offered by the competition. Obviously, a competitive advantage is gained by improving the product; the product or service can be differentiated by raising the level of customer satisfaction. However, a thorough analysis should always accompany any targeting of a product for customer satisfaction.

The goal is always to optimize customer satisfaction with resources. Raising the level of customer satisfaction too far beyond the current range is risky because of two factors. First, the cost factor could affect perceived value. Second, the customer might not be ready for the enhanced product or service. In each case, the product or service might not sell because it would not be satisfying the customer.

Know the competition

The organization must know the competition in order to establish targets for its products and services and internal improvement efforts.

The organization must establish product and service targets in relation to its competition. Typically organizations compete in the major areas of technology, cost, product quality, and service quality. Frequently product competition progresses from one area to the next area. It starts with technology, moves to cost, then product quality, then quality service, and so on.

For instance, when television first was marketed, technology was the foremost source of customer satisfaction. Once the technology was readily available and television had become more desirous to customers, price became the most important element. As the television became commonplace, customer satisfaction was judged by product quality. Today quality service is the differentiator.

The organization must identify the major area of competition where its product and services are competing. This will show the organization where to target its product and services. In addition, the organization would always attempt to achieve the competitive advantage. Therefore, it is important to look for ways to differentiate its product within the major area or areas of competition.

The organization must know where it is in relation to the competition to establish another kind of target, internal improvement effort targets. To determine its position in the competitive market, the organization should benchmark itself against its top competitor and best in the field.

Know your customers

Get to know your customers. They are not always obvious. Customers are all those touched by the product or service, whether internal or external to the organization. To continue to satisfy the customer, all customers must be identified.

Next, the target customers must be determined. Once specific customers are identified, customer needs and expectations must be determined. Customer expectations are dynamic; they continuously increase and change. This requires a continuous review of customer needs and expectations to ensure customer satisfaction. Like so much of TQM, this process, too, is continuous.

Identification of customer needs and expectations   The identification of customer needs and expectations requires systematic, thorough, and continuous marketing research. The most important aspect of this process is to listen to "the voice of the customer."

In addition to the tools and techniques described in chapters 6 through 10, such as customer analysis in chapter 7 and quality function deployment in chapter 10, some common marketing tools can help identify customer needs and expectations. These include media research, test marketing, customer auditing, and customer focus groups.

Changing customer needs   Customer needs are not static; they are always changing. Once customers needs are identified, these needs must be continuously monitored to ensure that the product and/or service still satisfies them. People have various needs, from basic survival needs such as eating and sleeping to the total fulfillment of a life goal. Customers satisfy lower-level needs before higher-level ones. A need once satisfied is often no longer a need.

Needs are constantly replaced by other needs because of the changing world environment. Rapidly changing technology, differing tastes, and rising expectations due to past successes are some of the many factors influencing customer changes.

Development of customer relationships   To ensure that the organization continues to satisfy the customer, a relationship with the customer is crucial. Relationships demand continuous attention. As Professor Theodore Levitt states in *The Marketing Imagination*,* "The sale merely consummates the courtship. Then the marriage begins. How good the marriage depends on how well the relationship is managed by the seller. That determines whether there will be continued or expanded business or troubles and divorce, and whether costs or profits increase." The emphasis is on keeping current customers while seeking additional customers for the future.

Like all relationships, customer relationships require communication, support, and responsiveness. Communication, especially listening, is essential. The customer needs to be involved in as many aspects of the product as possible. Support must be available to help the customer with the product after the product is received, and responsiveness is the key to continuing the relationship. The organization must be able to respond to the needs of the customer in any situation.

Key points

- A foundation of basic business ethics underlies all TQM efforts.
- Total Quality Management is the means to victories; TQM itself is not the victory. Always remember that the overall objective of TQM is to institutionalize the TQM philosophy and guiding principles in the everyday life of the organization.

---

*From *The Marketing Imagination* by Theodore Levitt, by permission of the author

- A systematic, integrated, consistent, organization-wide approach using action planning, training, and a support system are essential for victory.
- Strategic Total Quality Management Planning is the overall road map for creating and maintaining a TQM environment.
- TQM action planning provides the vehicle for focused action. Everyone in the organization must focus on specific actions that are continually measured, reviewed, and updated.
- The support system integrated into the organization guides the organization toward victory.
- Training gives the skills to accomplish the actions.
- Training should focus on the specific behaviors and skills required for work performance and TQM.
- A continuous improvement system is used to improve constantly the systems and processes in the organization.
- A continuous improvement system is eliminating waste, simplifying processes, and solving process problems.
- Measurement is the key to process improvement.
- The organization must maintain relationships with customer and supplier to ensure customer satisfaction.
- The continuous improvement system includes:
  ~ Defining the vision
  ~ Determining improvement opportunities
  ~ Selecting an improvement opportunity
  ~ Improving by using an improvement methodology
  ~ Evaluating the results
  ~ Repeating
- The focus of TQM is always total customer satisfaction, or quality.
- To achieve total customer satisfaction, the organization must:
  ~ Know itself
  ~ Know its product
  ~ Know the competition
  ~ Know the customer
- A continuous analysis of internal processes, the concept of the product, the competition, and customers is required.
- The organization should focus on maintaining current customers while striving to create customers for the future.

Part III

Improvement Methodology, its Tools and Techniques

5

Improvement methodology, tools and techniques

You will not succeed unless your men have tenacity and unity of purpose, and above all, a spirit of sympathetic cooperation.

Sun Tzu
Art of War

Within the continuous improvement system, an improvement methodology must be used for action planning, problem solving and process improvement. Chapter 4 discussed the continuous improvement system. This chapter covers the methodology for implementing improvement.

Organizations use many different improvement methodologies. These include statistical process control, quality function deployment, and process analysis. The improvement methodology must be geared to the specific organization. No matter what the improvement methodology, it should be used throughout the entire organization to create and maintain a systematic, integrated, consistent, organization-wide perspective.

The improvement methodology outlined in this book is useful for an organization. It combines commonly understood problem-solving methodology with the optional "plan, do, check, act" (PDCA) or Shewhart/Deming cycle. The basic problem-solving methodology instructs the user to understand, select, analyze, generate alternatives, select a solution, plan and gain approval, institute, and check. As mentioned, the PDCA or Shewhart/Deming cycle dictates to the user to plan, do, check, and act.

Basic improvement methodology

A basic eight-step improvement methodology is given below. Steps 1 through 8 are basic problem-solving methodology and can be continuously repeated. Steps 5a to d are optional and are used to test or pilot an improvement alternative (selected in step 5). They can be completely skipped. In this case, continue with step 6. However, it is recommended that you test or try the alternative on a pilot basis. Use steps 5a to d (note they are plan, do, check, act, or PDCA) to determine whether the alternative will provide the desired outcome without going through all the steps to institutionalize the improvement.

Basic improvement methodology steps

1. Understand/identify the opportunities.
2. Select an opportunity for improvement.
3. Analyze the selected opportunity.
4. Generate improvement alternatives.
5. Select an improvement alternative.
   a. Plan the improvement on a test or pilot basis.
   b. Do the improvement on a test or pilot basis.
   c. Check results of test or pilot against desired outcome.
   d. Act to make the improvement permanent or repeat, starting with 5a, or go back to step 1.
6. Plan and gain approval for the selected improvement.
7. Institute the selected improvement.
8. Check the results for the desired outcome.

Repeat these steps as many times as is necessary.

Using the basic improvement methodology for process improvement

The organization uses the basic improvement methodology throughout the entire organization for action planning, problem-solving, and process improvement. The basic improvement methodology is modified as appropriate for each specific application. An example of the basic methodology, modified for action planning, is described in chapter 4. The section above outlines problem-solving methodology.

Figure 5-1 shows another example of the basic improvement methodology, in this case modified for process improvement. The steps include understanding the process, selecting a critical process, analyzing the critical process, generating improvement alternatives, selecting an improvement and completing the PDCA cycle if feasible, planning and gaining approval, instituting the improvement, and checking the results.

Within the process improvement methodology, various tools and techniques are used. These tools and techniques are described in chapters 6 to 10.

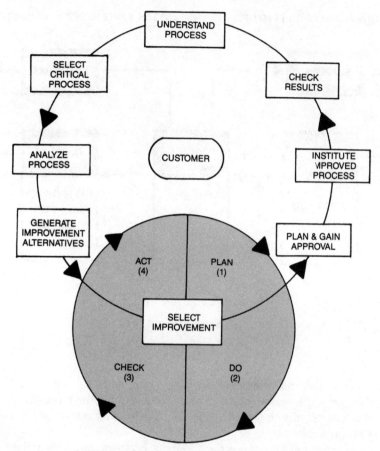

Fig. 5-1. Process improvement methodology.

The process

Before using the improvement methodology to improve a process, you should have an understanding of process definitions, the nature of a process, the states of a process, process measurement, and process variation.

Process definitions   The following are some basic definitions required to understand a process.

- A process is a series of activities that takes an input, modifies the input (work takes place and/or value is added), and produces an output. Thus, a process is the job itself. Figure 5-2 presents a graphic representation of a process.
- An input is what you need to do the job.
- An output is the product or service given to someone else.
- A supplier is the provider of the people, material, equipment, method, and/or environment that make up the input or inputs.

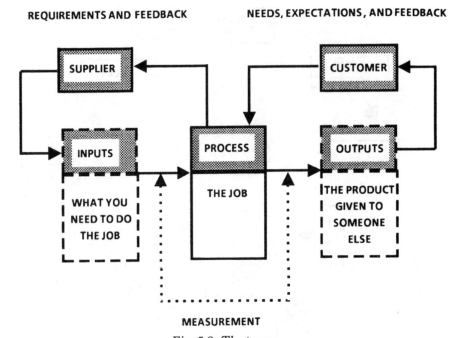

REQUIREMENTS AND FEEDBACK   **NEEDS, EXPECTATIONS, AND FEEDBACK**

Fig. 5-2. The process.

- A customer (internal or external) is anyone affected by the product or service.
- The owner is the person who is empowered to change the process.
- Continuous process improvement is the never-ending pursuit of excellence in process performance.
- A measurement of a process is the difference between the inputs and the outputs of the process as determined by the customer.
- A variation of a process is any deviation from its ultimate best target value.

The hierarchical nature of a process An understanding of the hierarchical nature of a process as displayed in FIG. 5-3 is important when improving a process. A process has many levels. At the top level of the figure are the three processes used to produce a part. A part is engineered, manufactured, and tested. Under manufacturing process is another level of processes. When manufacturing a part, a shop order is prepared, material kits are provided, the part is fabricated, and the part is inspected. The kitting process can be further broken down. Building a material kit requires pulling parts, preparing the kit, and releasing the kit to the shop.

Because of the various levels of processes, you should determine boundaries of a specific part or parts of a process. This means you must define the start and the finish. Further, processes impact other processes on the same level or on levels above or below them. Therefore, know the impact of any improvement effort on other processes before the improvement is implemented. For instance, if any improvement recommends making a square hole, a further process might be required to make a square peg.

Process states A process can be in one of several states shown in FIG. 5-4.

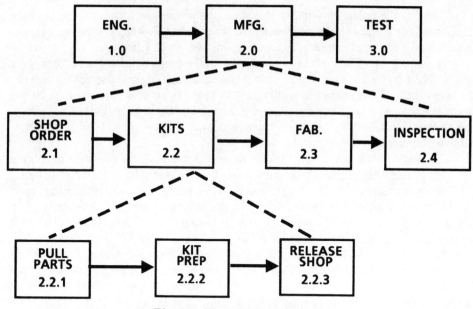

Fig. 5-3. The nature of a process.

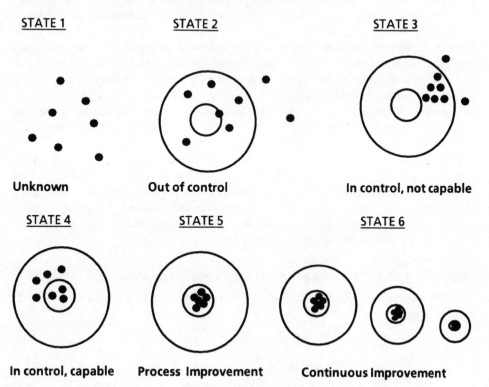

Fig. 5-4. Process states.

State 1 is the unknown state. In this state, the process performance has not been measured. State 2 shows the process out of control. In this state, the process performance is an element of chance; it cannot be predicted. State 3 displays a process in control but not capable. The process performance can be predicted, but the process is not within limits. State 4 is a process in control and capable. The process performance can be predicted, and the process is within limits. State 5 is process improvement. In this state, the process is improved to reduce variation from target value. State 6 is continuous improvement. In this state, the process is constantly improved to reach its best possible performance.

The continuous improvement system moves the process from one state to another with the ultimate aim of having the process perform consistently at its ultimate best.

Process management   All process performance can be measured through process indicators. Usually these process performance indicators are the difference between the input and the output of the process from a customer viewpoint. In manufacturing processes, the process performance indicators are called quality characteristics. These include such items as weight, height, thickness, strength, color, temperature, and density. Process performance indicators exist in every aspect of the organization. Some examples of process indicators are: errors, delivery time, number of orders filled, number of repairs, number of skilled personnel, response times, spares used, and time available for operational use.

Process variation   Variation exists in every process. The causes of variation are both common and special, or assignable. A common cause is the normal variation in an established process. It is always a part of the process. A special or assignable cause is an abnormal variation in the process arising from some particular circumstance. It is important to understand the impact of each cause of variation. A variation from a special or assignable cause should be solved as a specific problem attributed to something outside the normal process. A variation from a common cause can be improved only by a fundamental change in the process itself. If a common cause is mistaken for a special cause, an adjustment of the common cause could result in increased variation, frequently making the process worse.

For example, consider a test failure that is encountered when performing a final test of an assembly. The test failure is determined to be attributed to the "A" board. If the root cause of the failure is blamed on the special cause of operator error in the fabrication of the board, when in fact the procedures in the process were incorrect, which is a commmon cause, the test failure will be repeated in the future, regardless of any change in operator performance.

Improvement methodology for process improvement steps

The following steps outline in detail the use of the improvement methodology for process improvement:

Step 1   Understand the process.

During this first step, focus all efforts on understanding the specific contributions of the process to customer satisfaction. Specifically, to understand the process fully, do the following:

- Define the overall process.
- Diagram the top-level and top-down process.
- Specify the customer or customers of the process.
- List customer needs and expectations.
- Determine whether the process is meeting customer expectations.
- Discover who owns and influences the process.
- Determine all the inputs to and outputs from the process.
- Understand the relationship between inputs and outputs.
- List the suppliers of the inputs.
- Determine whether the suppliers are meeting the requirements.
- Determine how to measure the process.
- Measure the process to determine how it is performing.
- Understand the value of the process to the product or service.
- Determine whether the process can be eliminated.
- List the problems with the process as it exists.

Step 2 Select a critical process for improvement.

Select a critical process for improvement based on the information collected in the understanding stage. Often critical processes are not meeting the expectations of the customers. To select a part of a process for improvement, do the following:

- List areas of the process requiring improvement. This includes the parts of a process that are not meeting customer needs, inputs not meeting requirements, and problem areas.
- Specify the selection criteria.
- Determine the selection method.
- Define how the decision will be made.
- Make the decision.

Step 3 Analyze the selected critical process.

This requires a thorough use of analytical tools to focus on process variation or underlying causes of process problems. When analyzing the selected process part, do the following:

- Determine whether the whole process can be eliminated.
- Make a detailed list of the steps in the process.
- Diagram the process.
- Look for ways to eliminate non-value-added steps or to simplify the process.
- Eliminate or reduce wait times.
- Remove any unnecessary loops.
- Decrease any complexity.
- Analyze frequency changes.
- Eliminate or reduce any waste.
- Look for other ways to do the process.
- Find any problem areas.
- Determine the underlying cause.

- Define measurements.
- Find or collect data.
- Complete data gathering.
- Organize data.
- Define the expected outcome (goal or goals).
- Determine whether the process is meeting the goal.
- Analyze the forces at work in the situation.
- Determine the restraining forces.
- Specify the driving forces.

Step 4   Generate improvement alternatives.

During this step, use creativity, innovation, and imagination to explore as many alternatives as possible. When generating improvement alternatives, do the following:

- Define alternatives that can be used to reach the goal.
- Determine all the forces at play with each alternative.

Step 5   Select an improvement.

Select an improvement most likely to attain your desired outcome. If possible, complete the plan, do, check, act (PDCA) cycle as a test or pilot of the selected improvement; plan the pilot or test and do the improvement on a test or pilot basis. Check results against desired outcome. Act to make the improvement permanent. Specifically, do the following:

- Specify the selection criteria.
- Define the selection method.
- Determine how the decision will be made.
- Make the decision.
- Complete the PDCA cycle for the selected alternative, if feasible.

Step 6   Plan and gain approval for improvement.

This requires the preparation of a complete implementation plan. Further, a presentation might be needed to gain approval for implementation of the improvement. For this step, do the following:

- Determine how the improvement will be implemented.
- Prepare an implementation plan.
- Gain support.
- Stress benefits.
- Determine whether a presentation is required.
- Prepare the presentation.
- Request action in the presentation.
- Overcome objections during the presentation.
- Follow up on actions after the presentation.

Step 7   Institute the improvement.

This step involves institutionalizing the improvement. Specifically, do the following:

- Install a continuous feedback system.
- Develop, document, and implement procedures.
- Provide training if necessary.

Step 8 Check the results for the desired outcome.

At this step, continuously check results to ensure that the process is staying under control. If the process is not meeting desired outcomes, return to step 1 (understand), step 3 (analyze), or step 4 (generate alternatives). Repeat all of the steps, 1 through 8, as many times as necessary to achieve the overall goal or goals. During this step, do the following:

- Measure the performance against the expected outcome (goal or goals).
- Determine whether you are meeting those goals.
- Continue to keep the process under control.
- Continuously improve the process.

Improvement tools and techniques

If you know the enemy and know yourself, you need not fear the result of a hundred battles. If you know yourself but not the enemy, for every victory gained you will suffer a defeat. If you know neither the enemy or yourself, you will succumb in every battle.

Sun Tzu
Art of War

A continuous improvement methodology using the appropriate tools and techniques is an essential element of Total Quality Management. By using an orderly approach, as is done in the continuous improvement methodology, processses are improved. It is important that everyone know where they are going and how they are going to get there. The continuous improvement cycle provides the methodology to accomplish this.

Equally important is using proven tools and techniques within the continuous improvement cycle and improvement methodology. The latter part of this chapter describes some areas in which specific tools and techniques can be effective within improvement methodology. However, each organization and individual is encouraged to use the tools and techniques in any way appropriate to the specific applications. Further, the tools and techniques can be tailored to your specific application. If it works, use it.

Many tools and techniques are available for improvement. The most common are described in this book. For organizational purposes, they are arranged in the following categories: people involvement, process understanding, selection, analysis, and system improvement.

People involvement

People involvement is one of the key tools of Total Quality Management. People involvement includes both individual and group activities. Unlike other categories of tools and techniques, that of people involvement has many subdivisions. They include individual involvement, teams, teamwork, communication, listening, goal setting, meetings, brainstorming, the nominal group technique, and presentation. People involvement is described in chapter 6. The following is a brief description of each tool:

- *Individual involvement*

  Individual involvement is the involvement of each person in the organization in the work itself and in the improvement of the work.

- *Team*

  A team is a group of people working together for a common goal.

- *Teamwork*

  Teamwork is a technique where the individual members of a team work together to achieve a common goal.

- *Communication*

  Communication is any technique used for exchanging information.

- *Listening*

  Listening is a form of communication for receiving and understanding information.

- *Focus setting*

  Focus setting is a technique used to focus on a specified outcome.

- *Meeting*

  A meeting is a tool for bringing a group together to work for a common goal.

- *Brainstorming*

  Brainstorming is a tool that encourages the collective thinking power of a group in order to create ideas.

- *Nominal group technique*

  Nominal group technique, like brainstorming, provides structured discussion and decision making.

- *Presentation*

  Presentation is a tool for providing information, gaining approval, or requesting action.

Process understanding

Process understanding tools and techniques are essential to the improvement methodology. They include benchmarking, process diagrams, input/output analysis, and supplier/customer analysis. These tools are outlined in chapter 7. The following is a brief description of each tool:

- *Benchmarking*

  Benchmarking is a method of measuring your organization against those of recognized leaders.

- *Process diagrams*

  A process diagram is a tool for defining the process.

- *Input/output analysis*

  Input/output analysis is a technique for identifying interdependency problems.

- *Supplier/customer analysis*

  Supplier/customer analysis is a technique used to obtain and exchange information for conveying your needs and requirements to suppliers and mutually determining the needs and expectations of your customers.

Selection

Selection tools and techniques are used several times during the improvement methodology to help clarify assumptions and focus on consensus when selecting an improvement opportunity or improvement. The selection tools and techniques are voting, selection matrix, and selection grid. These tools are outlined in chapter 8. The following is a brief description of each tool:

- *Voting*

  Voting is a technique for determining majority opinion.

- *Selection matrix*

  A selection matrix is a tool for rating problems, opportunities, or alternatives according to specific criteria.

- *Selection grid*

  A selection grid is a tool for comparing each problem, opportunity, or alternative against all others.

Analysis

During the improvement methodology, a thorough analysis is extremely important. The tools and techniques for analysis help improve the process, determine underlying causes, identify the vital few causes, and describe both sides of an issue. The analysis tools and techniques are process analysis, cause-and-effect analysis, data collection and analysis, and force field analysis. These tools are outlined in chapter 9. The following is a brief description of each tool:

- *Process analysis*

  Process analysis is a tool to improve the process and reduce process cycle time by eliminating non-value-added activities and/or simplifying the process.

- *Cause-and-effect analysis*

  Cause-and-effect analysis is a technique for helping a group examine underlying causes.

- *Data statistical analysis*

  Data statistical analysis is a combination of several tools for collecting, sorting, charting, and analyzing data.

- *Force field analysis*

  Force field analysis is a technique that describes the forces at work in a given situation.

System improvement

System improvement tools and techniques focus on the development or redesign of systems, specifically on the improvement of the product and/or service itself. System improvement tools are outlined in chapter 10. The following is a brief description of each tool:

- *Concurrent engineering*

  Concurrent engineering is a systematic approach to the integrated, concurrent design of products and their related processes, including manufacture and support. This approach is intended to cause the developers, from the outset, to consider all elements of the product life cycle from conception through disposal, including quality, cost, schedule, and user requirements.

- *Quality function deployment*

  Quality function deployment is a disciplined approach for transforming customer requirements, the voice of the customer, into product development requirements.

- *Robust design*

  Robust design is a technique for designing a product for minimal quality losses.

- *Design of experiments*

  Design of experiments is a tool used to establish both parametric relationships and a product/process model in the early (applied research) stages of the design process.

- *Taguchi approach*

  The Taguchi approach includes several techniques for reducing the variation of product or process performance to minimize loss.

- *Cost of quality*

  Cost of quality techniques are used to identify the cost of conformance and nonconformance.

- *Cost of poor quality*

  Cost of poor quality techniques focus on minimizing the cost of nonconformance.

- *Statistical process control*

  Statistical process control is a statistical tool for monitoring and controlling a process in order to maintain and possibly improve quality.

Use of tools and techniques

Total Quality Management tools and techniques can be used in many places within the improvement methodology. Below are recommendations for the use of tools and techniques during specific steps of the process improvement methodology.

Tools and techniques for specific uses

Understanding the process   The following tools and techniques are useful when understanding the process:

- Focus setting
- Input/output analysis
- Process analysis
- Brainstorming
- Process diagrams
- Supplier/customer analysis
- Data statistical analysis
- Nominal group technique

Selecting a critical process of improvement   The following selection tools and techniques help clarify assumptions and focus on consensus when selecting a part of the process for improvement:

- Voting
- Selection grid
- Selection matrix
- Decision making

Analyzing the selected critical process   The following tools and techniques are useful when analyzing the selected part:

- Process diagrams
- Cause-and-effect analysis
- Focus setting
- Process analysis
- Force field analysis
- Data statistical analysis

Generating improvement alternatives   Use one of the following tools and techniques when generating alternatives:

- Brainstorming
- Force field analysis
- Nominal group technique

Selecting improvement   The following tools and techniques help clarify assumptions and focus on consensus when selecting an alternative:

- Voting
- Selection grid
- Selection matrix
- Decision making

Planning and gaining approval   The following tools and techniques assist with planning and gaining approval for the selected improvement:

- Force field analysis
- Presentation

Instituting the selected improvements   The following tools and techniques are useful when implementing selected improvement:

- Continuous feedback system
- Development of document
- Procedure implementation
- Training

Checking the results for the desired outcome   The following tools and techniques help check the results against the desired outcome:

- Data/statistical analysis
- Supplier/customer analysis

Key points

- The improvement methodology is used within the continuous improvement system to accomplish the mission, improve the process improvement, and solve problems.
- The basic improvement methodology is:
  - ~ Understand.
  - ~ Select.
  - ~ Analyze.
  - ~ Generate alternatives.

~ Select improvement. Optional steps for a test or pilot include plan, do, check, act (PDCA).
~ Plan and gain approval.
~ Institute.
~ Check results.
~ Repeat.
• The basic improvement methodology can be used for process improvement.
• A process includes input, the process itself, and output. A supplier provides the input or inputs to the process. The owner is responsible for the process and has the authority to act. The customer receives the outputs of the process.
• Every process has some degree of variability. The aim is to eliminate or reduce this variation.
• Variation is caused by common or special causes. Determine the type of cause before pursuing corrective action.
• Focus on the process; do not look for blame or fault in the people.
• There are tools and techniques for all phases of the improvement methodology and system improvements.
• The categories of tools and techniques are:
~ People involvement
~ Process understanding
~ Selection
~ Process analysis
~ System improvement
• The tools and techniques should be used as appropriate within the improvement methodology to provide the most benefit to the specific organization.
• System improvement tools and techniques are aimed primarily at quality of design and prevention of defects.

6

People involvement
tools and techniques

Unhappy is the fate of one who tries to win his battles and succeed in his attacks without cultivating the spirit of enterprise, for the result is waste of time and general stagnation. The enlightened ruler lays his plans well ahead; the good general cultivates his resources. He controls his soldiers by his authority, knits them together by good faith, and by rewards makes them serviceable. If faith decays, there will be disruption; if rewards are deficient, commands will not be respected.

Sun Tzu
Art of War

People are the key to victory in the Total Quality Management environment. Since people make up organizations, they can have a positive or a negative effect on the performance of the organization. Traditionally, organizations have focused on minimizing the negative effect of people. Total Quality Management tries to maximize the positive benefits from people. This is accomplished by fostering both individual and team contributions to the organization. In addition, teamwork, communication, and listening are essential. Further, the tools and techniques of focus setting, meetings, brainstorming, nominal group technique, and presentations achieve results.

Individual involvement

Individual involvement concerns each person's contributions to the organization. Individuals work to continually perform their duties and improve the processes in the organization, with the focus on total customer satisfaction.

Individual involvement in an organization depends on many factors in order to include the differences and similarities of people. To maximize the benefit of people, it is essential to understand that people are different in many respects but that they want the same, basic things.

Every individual is different from every other individual. Each has unique values, attitudes, personality, beliefs, behaviors, perceptions, education, experience, abilities, culture, goals, social needs, and economic expectations. These differences provide the organization with its particular potential. Individual differences are the primary source of creativity and innovation that can be a major competitive advantage. In a TQM organization, individual differences are valued as an important resource.

Although each person is different, people generally want some of the same, basic things. They want to be safe and secure; to belong; to feel trusted, appreciated, and important; and to have both involvement and advancement opportunities and pride in work. The organization that provides a work environment where all of these wants and needs can be attained by the individual is rewarded with high individual involvement and productivity.

In a TQM environment, the goal of people involvement is the actual empowerment of everyone in the organization. Empowerment means all individuals in the organization have the authority to do whatever is necessary to perform and improve their work. Typically, people involvement in organizations goes through stages. First there is participation, then involvement, and finally empowerment.

In order to foster individual involvement:

Instill pride of workmanship.
Nurture individual self-esteem.
Develop an atmosphere of trust and encouragement.
Involve everyone.
Visualize a common purpose.
Improve everything.
Demand effective and open communications.
Use reward and recognition.
Allow creativity and innovation.
Lead by example.

Individual involvement steps

1. Establish the TQM environment (see chapter 3).
2. Provide training and coaching.
3. Provide opportunities to experience expected behavior.
4. Reward and recognize appropriate behavior.

The skillfull general conducts his army just as though he were
leading a single man by the hand.

Sun Tzu
Art of War

Teams

Teams are made up of people working together for a common goal. They are an essential structural ingredient of Total Quality Management. Teams are needed to meet the challenges of the new environment; they meet these challenges with:

Becoming better at decision making
Enticing everyone to participate
Nurturing relationships
Encouraging rewards in the work itself
Fitting any organization
Increasing communication
Thrusting an organization toward awareness of the vision
Supporting a systematic integration of the organization

Team types

Teams can be either functional or multifunctional. Functional teams involve people from one functional group. Multifunctional teams consist of members from many different functional areas. In addition, teams can be work teams or improvement teams. Work teams actually perform the work. Improvement teams are formed solely to improve a process. Usually, work teams have the task of performing and improving the work, whereas improvement teams focus only on improvement.

Team tasks

Specifically, teams do the following:

- Perform the work
- Apply a structured improvement methodology to meet a goal or goals
- Define and improve a process
- Identify supplier requirements and customer expectations
- Identify improvement opportunities
- Develop process performance goals and measurements
- Collect and analyze data
- Determine a solution or solutions
- Create an action plan
- Take action
- Present recommendations

Team stages

Normally, teams go through several stages on the way to success. The duration and intensity of each stage varies with each team. Most teams must go through all the stages before reaching synergy. However, it is important to maintain a positive attitude throughout all the stages: the team will achieve its goal.

Stage 1

During the first stage, the team has great enthusiasm for accomplishing its goal. Members are building rapport.

Stage 2

This stage is characterized by being overwhelmed by the information and the task. Stage 2 is the most difficult. Some teams never progress past this stage; if this happens, they should disband. However, to move forward to the next stage, a team must find some small success as a group. Once the team understands they can perform as a team, the team usually progresses to the next stage.

Stage 3

During stage 3, the team moves toward the goal. In this stage customer contact and measurements can help the team members start to assist each other and focus on the goal.

Stage 4

Finally, in stage 4 the team becomes effective. The team members work together to achieve the goal. This pattern is repeated in most teams.

Teamwork

Teamwork is a technique in which the individual team members work together to achieve a common goal. This involves cooperative relationships, open communications, group problem solving, and group decision making. Specifically, effective teamwork involves the following:

Training—Ensure training; teamwork, tools, techniques, skills.
Everyone—Involve everyone in the team.
Action—Focus on the mission/goal.
Management—Get commitment and support.
We—Communicate, cooperate, and collaborate.
Opportunities—Match individual and organizational growth.
Reward and recognition—Recognize success.
Knowledge—Understand the improvement process.

In order to build and maintain teamwork, observe the same TQM principles: ensure that the team is operating in a TQM environment, involving all members in an atmosphere of trust and open communications. Respect individual identity and always consider individual self-esteem by encouraging all team members to contribute. Listen effectively at all times. Above all, focus on the problems, opportunities, goal, and mission—not the person.

Communication

Communication is the exchange of information. Communicating the right information is vital to success. However, communication is a complex process including many verbal and nonverbal forms. Because of this complexity, information might be communicated incorrectly. Therefore, it is critical to verify through feedback the right information has been communicated.

Improving communication

The communication process can be improved by doing the following:

Clarify the message.
Observe body language.
Maintain everyone's self-esteem.
Make your point short and simple.
Understand the viewpoints of others.
Nurture others' feelings.
Involve yourself in the message.
Comprehend the message.
Attend to the message of others.
Talk judiciously.
Emphasize listening.

Listening

Listening is a technique for receiving and understanding information. Listening skills are critical to effective teamwork. Effective listening requires an effort in order to understand the ideas and feelings the other person is trying to communicate. That is, good listening requires active behavior. It requires attention to the person and the message. It also means communicating that you are listening and trying to understand the other person.

Effective listening requires the following:

Let the other person convey his or her message.
Involve yourself in the message.
Summarize and paraphrase frequently.
Talk only to clarify.
Empathize with the other's views.
Nurture active listening skills.

Let the other person convey his or her message   Let the other person convey his or her message without interrupting and without forcing your own views. This is accomplished by letting the other person know you are interested in what he or she is communicating without displaying an opinion or judgment.

Involve yourself in the message   Involve yourself in the message by actively listening to what the other person is communicating. Establish and maintain eye contact. Keep an alert posture. Look for verbal and nonverbal clues.

Summarize and paraphrase frequently   By summarizing and paraphrasing frequently, you show an understanding of the message. Also, by listening carefully and then rephrasing in your own words the content and feelings of the other person's message, you can make sure you have understood the exact meaning of the message.

Talk only to clarify   Ask questions to clarify points you do not understand. Points can be clarified by using open-ended questions: a question with an answer other than yes or no provides you with a more detailed explanation.

Empathize with other's views   Understanding the other person's views is essential to effective listening. Set aside your opinions and judgments and put yourself in the other person's place. Show the other person that you understand by requesting more information or by sharing a similar feeling or experience you have had and how you think it helps you understand the other person.

Nurture active listening skills   Nurture listening skills to improve communication. Listening skills must be practiced daily.

Focus setting

Focus setting is a technique used by teams to focus a specific outcome. In order to achieve results, teams must focus on their specific mission. While achieving this they must always strive for excellence while satisfying the customer. The mission of the team is the focus. This focus must be agreed to by the team. The focus is usually a mission that normally is stated in general terms. To accomplish the mission, the team must also determine the specific desired outcomes, or the team goal.

Mission

The mission is the general intended result. A team should state the mission in a results-oriented form.

Mission examples   Figure 6-1 shows an example of a mission statement. Other examples of a mission statement are as follows:

- Provide the product on schedule.
- Eliminate errors in order processing.
- Decrease cost of manufacturing.
- Improve assembly workmanship.
- Reduce failure rates of circuit boards.

MISSION

REDUCE THE TIME AND COST REQUIRED TO RETURN A
DEFECTIVE PART TO THE VENDOR

Fig. 6-1. Example of a mission statement.

Goal

The goal is the specific desired outcome. It should be not only specific but measurable, attainable, results oriented, and time bound. Set a reasonable goal or goals, but do not set your sights too low: set a goal that will be a challenge. Orient goals to specific, measurable results and link goals to customer requirements.

Gear to specific results; define within specific parameters.
Observe by measurement to check outcome.
Attain success through challenge that includes built-in success.
Limit to a specific time period.
Set by individual or group that makes it happen.

Goal example Figure 6-2 provides an example of a goal. Some other examples of goals are as follows:

- Reduce manufacturing cycle time for assembly X from 6 to 2 hours within 1 month.
- Decrease the errors in the "quantity required" block on the order processing sheet from 10 per month to 0 in 3 months.
- Reduce rework on process A from 50 to 20 percent in 2 months.

Fig. 6-2. Example of a goal.

> **GOAL**
>
> DECREASE DEFECTIVE PARTS DELIVERY TIME FROM THE MANUFACTURING SHOP, BUILDING 200, TO SHIPPING, BUILDING 118, FROM 2 DAYS TO 12 HOURS WITHIN 3 MONTHS.

Focus-setting steps

1. Define the mission.
2. Determine improvement opportunities.
3. Select an opportunity for improvement.
4. Set goal or goals to accomplish the mission.
5. Use improvement methodology within the continuous improvement cycle.

Meetings

Meetings are a technique used to bring a team together to work for a common goal. Effective meetings are an important aspect of getting a group to develop improvements that an individual could not come up with. By bringing together people in a meeting to develop improvements for a common goal, better decisions can result.

To make the meeting effective requires an action-oriented focus. All members of the team must have a common focus and methodology geared toward specific actions.

In addition, actions must be taken before, during, and after the meeting to ensure the proper preparation, conduct, and follow-up. A meeting agenda, as shown in FIG. 6-3, provides a mean for ensuring that everyone knows what to expect during the meeting. It also provides desired outcomes and action items with follow-up.

MEETING AGENDA

NAME OF TEAM:	**DATE:**
START TIME:	**END TIME:**

DESIRED OUTCOME(S):

LEADER:
MEMBERS:

AGENDA:		
ITEM	RESPONSIBLE PERSON	TIME

ACTION ITEMS:		
ACTION	ACTION PERSON	STATUS

Fig. 6-3. Sample of a meeting agenda.

Initial meeting actions

It is important to get the team started correctly. During the first meeting, the following should be accomplished:

- Establish rules of conduct.
- Understand the mission/goal of the team.
- Establish an agenda.

Rules of conduct

It is important to provide guidance for the team's conduct. The team establishes rules of conduct during the first team meeting by consensus and posts them during every team activity. These rules can be changed any time the team determines it is necessary. However, establishing the rules by consensus in the first meeting helps build rapport through a nonthreatening task.

Rely on facts, not opinions.
Understand others' points of view.
Listen actively to all ideas.
Encourage others.
Submit assignments on time.

Before the meeting

The success of the team depends on the active involvement of all team members in all meetings. The following are some meaningful guidelines to assist the team in conducting an effective meeting:

- Review the agenda.
- Gather information about the problem.
- Review what you know about the problem.
- Analyze the problem.
- Determine possible solutions.
- Prepare with an open mind.
- Complete all assignments.

At the meeting—speaking

Share information, but be concise.
Plan what you are going to say before you talk.
Encourage building on your ideas.
Avoid personal remarks. Shoot at an idea, not a person.
Keep your remarks focused on the subject.
Involve yourself. Remember, silence gives consent.
Nurture the ideas of others.
Generate ideas with short questions, not long statements.

At the meeting—cooperate

Consider the self-esteem of others.
Operate with the group. Give others a fair hearing.
Observe others' reactions.
Pursue a common focus.
Establish open communications.
Recognize individual contributions.
Allow positive conflict.
Trade off ideas with the group.
Encourage trust.

After the meeting

- Perform assignments and/or action items.
- Maintain group integrity and ethics.
- Keep a record of important data and actions.

Brainstorming

Brainstorming is a technique used by a group of people that encourages their collective thinking power for the purpose of generating ideas.

Brings out the most ideas in the shortest time.
Reduces the need to give correct answers.
Allows the group to have fun.
Increases involvement and participation.
Nurtures positive thinking.
Solicits varying ideas and concepts.
Tempers negative attitudes.
Omits criticism and evaluation of ideas.
Results in improved solutions.
Maximizes the attainment of goals.

Rules

Record all ideas.
Use exaggerations and wild suggestions.
Limit judgment until later.
Encourage idea building.
Solicit quantity.

Procedures

The three primary brainstorming methods are:

- Round robin
- Free-wheeling
- Slip

Each has advantages and disadvantages that the group or discussion leader must weigh before determining which would best accomplish the desired results. In some cases, the best method may be a combination of the various brainstorming methods. For instance, a brainstorming session may start with a round robin or slip method and move into a free-wheeling method to add more ideas.

Round robin method   With this method each group member in turn contributes an idea as it relates to the purpose of the discussion. Every idea is recorded on a flip chart or board. When a group member has nothing to contribute, he or she simply says, "pass." The next time around, this person may offer an idea or pass again. Ideas are solicited until no one has anything to add.

Round robin advantages

- It is difficult for one person to dominate the discussion.
- Everyone is given an opportunity to participate fully.

Round robin disadvantage

- People feel frustration while waiting their turn.

Free-wheeling method   Each team member calls out ideas freely and in a random order. Every idea is recorded on a flip chart or board. The process continues until no one has anything else to add.

Free-wheeling advantage

- This procedure is spontaneous and has no restrictions.

Free-wheeling disadvantages

- Some individuals may dominate.
- Quiet team members may be reluctant to speak.
- It might be chaotic if too many people talk at the same time.

Slip method   Each team member writes all of his or her ideas on an issue, a problem, or an alternative on a piece of paper. He or she writes as many ideas as possible. Then the slips are collected, and all the ideas are written on the board. A variation of this method is the Crawford Slip method, in which each idea is written on a separate slip of paper. The slips are then put on a board and arranged in categories.

Slip method advantage

- All ideas are recorded, and all contributions are anonymous.

Slip method disadvantages

- Some creativity may be lost because of the inability of some team members to react to the contributions of others.

Brainstorming example   Figure 6-4 provides an example of a brainstorming session on the barriers to teamwork.

BARRIERS TO TEAMWORK

1.   Personality Conflicts

2.   Egos

3.   Management

4.   Management styles

5.   Language

6.   Communication

7.   Not listening

8.   Shy person

9.   Lack of motivation

10. Dominant person

11. Lack of interest

12. Lack of technical language

13. Participation

14. Caste system

15. Not respecting others individual identity

16. Closed mind

17. Not a priority

18. Not familiar with the subject

Fig. 6-4. Results of a brainstorming session.

Nominal group technique

Nominal group technique is a refinement of brainstorming. It provides a more structured discussion and decision-making technique.

Nominal group technique steps

1. Present the issue and give instructions.
2. Allow time for idea generation.
3. Gather ideas via a round robin, one at a time. Write each idea on a flip chart or board. Post the board.
4. Process or clarify ideas. Focus on clarifying meaning, not arguing points. Eliminate duplicate ideas; combine similar ones.
5. Set priorities.

Presentation

Sometimes a presentation may be necessary to provide information, obtain approval, or request action. The presentation may be given formally or informally by the team. Involve as many team members as possible in the actual presentation.

A presentation also provides the opportunity to inform its audience of team activities and accomplishments and to recognize team members for their contributions.

Presentation Steps

Step 1 Gain support.

Gaining support requires identifying and involving key people early in the improvement process. Ensure support for a team recommendation from owners, suppliers, and customers by stressing its benefits.

Step 2 Prepare for the presentation.
- Know the audience.
- Understand how the recommendation affects others.
- Outline the benefits.
- Anticipate objections.
- Rehearse the presentation.
- Arrange the presentation.

Step 3 Give the presentation.
- Build rapport.
- Make the recommendation.
- Stress the benefits.
- Overcome objections.
- Seek action.

Step 4 Follow up after the presentation.
- Follow up to ensure that the recommended action is taken.
- Reduce postdecision anxiety by repeating and summarizing benefits.
- Stress the importance of early implementation.

Key points

- People are the key to victory in a Total Quality Management environment.
- Individuals' work involves continually performing their jobs and improving the processes in the organization, with the focus on customer satisfaction.
- People are different in many respects, but they want the same, basic things.
- The empowerment of all people in the organization to do whatever is necessary to perform and improve their work is the ultimate goal of people involvement.
- Teams working for a common goal are essential ingredients of Total Quality Management.
- Teamwork involves cooperative relationships, open communications, and group problem solving and decision making.
- Communication and sharing of information is vital to success.
- Listening is the most important communication skill.
- All groups must be focused to achieve results.
- Effective meetings are a helpful technique for bringing a group together to work for a common goal.
- The collective thinking power of a team can be encouraged through the use of brainstorming and/or the nominal group technique.
- Brainstorming and/or the nominal group technique is effective whenever the group requires stimulation.
- Presentations are an effective tool for getting action.

7

Process understanding tools and techniques

What enables the wise sovereign and good general to strike and conquer, and achieve things beyond the reach of ordinary men, is foreknowledge.

Sun Tzu
Art of War

The first step in any improvement effort is understanding the process. A thorough understanding not only has a great impact on the effectiveness of the rest of the improvement process but also is necessary before continuing to any other step in the improvement methodology.

To ensure that the organization is performing the right processes, satisfying the right customer, aiming at the right target, and requesting accurate requirements of suppliers, process understanding is critical.

Several tools and techniques are available to assist in process understanding. Benchmarking helps determine goals based on the accomplishments of recognized leaders in the field. Process diagrams define the process. Input/output analysis identifies interdependency problems. Supplier/customer analysis helps obtain and exchange information for conveying your requirements to suppliers and mutually determining the needs and expectations of your customers. This chapter discusses these tools and techniques.

Benchmarking

Benchmarking is a method of measuring your organization against the recognized best performers in a certain industry, organization, function, system, or process. The purpose of benchmarking is to provide a target for improved performance. Benchmarking:

Brings the focus on improvement efforts
Emphasizes desired outcomes
Nurtures competitiveness
Creates the desire to be the best
Holds the organization together
Measures critical areas
Analyzes critical areas against the best
Reinforces continuous improvement
Keeps everyone on target

Benchmarking steps

The steps in benchmarking are the following:

1. Understand your organization.
2. Select critical areas for benchmarking.
3. Determine where to get benchmark information.
4. Collect and analyze data.
5. Select target benchmarks.
6. Determine your performance.
7. Set desired outcomes.
8. Use improvement methodology to achieve desired performance.

Process diagram

A process diagram is a tool for defining a process that is a major focus for improvement activity. An initial step in any improvement activity should be to define and understand the process. Each organization, function, and person should define his or her specific process (or processes) and understand how the process satisfies the needs and expectations of both internal and external customers. Each process is a customer of the preceding process, and each process also has a customer. Everyone must constantly strive to improve his or her process both as a customer and for a customer.

A process diagram uses symbols and words to describe a process. This type of diagram provides an indication or improvement opportunities, non-value-added tasks, and places where simplification of a process is possible.

Process—A series of related tasks
Requirements—What you need to communicate to suppliers
Owner—The person who is empowered to change the process
Customer—Everyone who is affected by the product/service
Expectations—What to provide to your customers
Supplier—The provider of inputs to the process
System—Many processes

Determine the details of the diagram.
Identify the interrelationships of the process.
Analyze the results of the process.
Graphically display the process.
Reexamine roles and relationships.
Assess which elements impact process performance.
Measure the process.

The three types of process diagrams are:

- Top-level process diagram
- Top-down process diagram
- Detailed process diagram

Top-level process diagram

A top-level process diagram is a picture of the entire process. This type of process diagram shows the input or inputs, the process, and the output or outputs of the process. A top-level process diagram should focus on satisfying customers' needs and expectations. The expected results must be determined, and the process must be measured to determine whether it is achieving results. Figure 7-1 shows a top-level process diagram of a system development process.

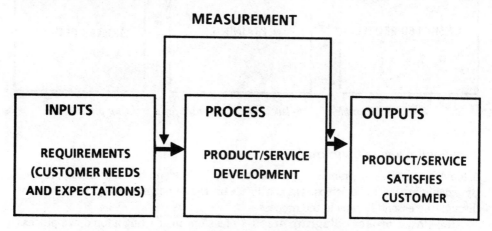

Fig. 7-1. Top-level process diagram.

Top-level process diagram steps   The steps for creating a top-level process diagram are:

1. Define the specific outcome of the process, focusing on the customer.
2. State the process in terms of the work that must be done to achieve the desired outcome.
3. Determine the input or inputs required to satisfy the customer.
4. Measure the process. This measurement is usually the difference between inputs and outputs.

5. Analyze how the process is performing at the top level.
6. Use improvement methodology within the continuous improvement cycle.

Top-level process diagram example   An analysis of a system development process reveals that the customer expects the product to be repaired in minimum time. This requires that we have trained technicians to service our product. The top-level process diagram in FIG. 7-2 shows the training process. The training process takes the unskilled people who enter the process and transforms them into skilled people. Before the people enter training, a pretest is administered to determine entry-level skills. At the completion of training, a posttest is given to determine the overall effectiveness of training. This is the measurement of the process. The training process is then continually checked and improved using the continuous improvement cycle.

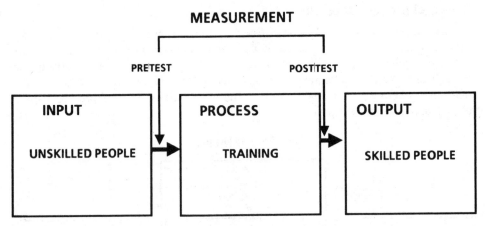

Fig. 7-2. Example of a top-level process diagram for a training process.

Top-down process diagram

A top-down process diagram is a chart of the major steps and substeps in the process. By examining the major steps, we can focus on the opportunities for improvement through the essential steps in the process.

Top-down process diagram steps   The steps in charting a top-down process diagram are:

1. List the major steps in the process. List no more than seven steps.
2. List the major substeps. Keep each sublist at no more than seven steps.

Top-down process flow diagram example   Still using the example of training workers, list the major steps in the top-down process. As shown in FIG. 7-3A, these steps would include: conduct, analysis, prepare training design, develop strategy and materials, present training, conduct evaluations, and perform continuous improvement. Once you have determined the major steps, list the major substeps for each major step, as shown in FIG. 7-3B. To conduct an analysis, the following must be performed: identify

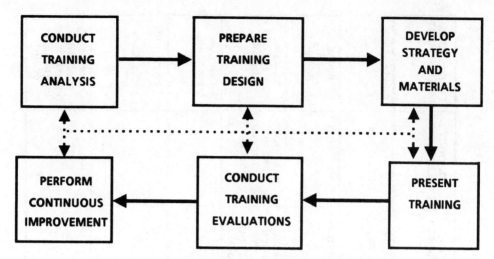

Fig. 7-3A. Top-down process flow diagram.

instructional goal or goals, determine behaviors to meet the goal or goals, write instructional goal, conduct task analysis, identify entry behaviors and skills and check the analysis to ensure it meets instructional goals. Write substeps for the other major steps. The final step in all processes is the continuous improvement of the process. In the example, this involves the following: redoing the analysis, revising training design, updating training strategy and materials, improving the presentation of the course, reviewing and updating evaluations, and the constant checking to ensure that the training meets the goal or goals.

Detailed process diagram

A detailed process diagram is a flowchart consisting of symbols and words that completely describe a process. This type of diagram provides information that indicates improvement opportunities, identifies areas for data analysis, determines which elements impact process performance, and documents and standardizes the process. It is helpful for identifying non-value-added tasks and areas for simplification. Further, complex activities and unnecessary loops are visualized. This type of process diagram is useful for training and for explaining the process to others.

Before deciding to do a detailed process diagram, decide on the specific details and boundaries of the process diagram. Detailed process diagrams are time consuming. Therefore, specific boundaries are important to ensure progress in achieving improvements.

Detailed process diagram basic symbols Because many detailed process diagram symbols are used, four basic symbols are recommended for simplicity. These symbols, shown in FIG. 7-4, are sufficient for most process diagramming needs. The four basic detailed process diagram symbols are as follows:

- The beginning or end of a process is shown by squares with rounded sides.
- Decision statements are written in diamonds. A decision statement asks a yes or

PROCESS: TECHNICAL TRAINING

MAJOR STEPS	CONDUCT ANALYSIS	PREPARE TRAINING DESIGN	DEVELOP STRATEGY AND MATERIALS	PRESENT TRAINING	CONDUCT EVALUATIONS	CONTINUOUS IMPROVEMENT
Substep 1	Identify instructional goal(s)	Write terminal objective(s)	Determine outline of instruction	Conduct course verification	Conduct course evaluations	Redo analysis
Substep 2	Determine behaviors to meet goal(s)	Write enabling objectives to meet terminal objective(s)	Determine time requirements	Conduct course	Present tests	Revise training design
Substep 3	Write instructional goal	Identify exact performance required	Determine training strategy	Check instruction meeting instructional goal(s)	Check results meeting instructional goal(s)	Update strategy and materials
Substep 4	Conduct task analysis	Write test questions to measure each objective	Select training materials			Improve presentation
Substep 5	Identify entry behaviors and skills	Check objectives and test items meeting instructional goal(s)	Prepare training materials			Review and update evaluations
Substep 6	Check analysis		Check strategy and materials to meet instructional goal(s)			Continuously check and revise to meet instructional goal(s)

Fig. 7-3B. Top-down diagram work sheet.

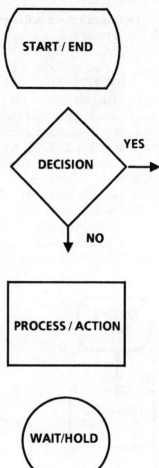

*Fig. 7-4. Basic symbols for
detailed process diagrams.*

no question. If the answer is yes, the path labeled yes is followed; otherwise the no path is followed.

*   Action statements are written in rectangles or squares.
*   Wait/hold is illustrated by a circle.

Detailed process diagram steps   Use these steps to complete a detailed process diagram:

1. Decide on the specific details and boundaries of the detailed process diagram.
2. List all steps required in the process within the boundaries.
3. Construct a process flow diagram.
4. Determine the times and cost of each activity.

Detailed process diagram example A detailed process diagram example is shown in FIG. 7-5. It consists of the following activities:

1. A Subcontractor Data Requirements List (SDRL) is received by Materials (INPUT).
2. Materials forwards the SDRL to Data Management (ACTION).
3. Data Management logs the SDRL (ACTION).
4. Data Management determines whether an internal review is required before distribution (DECISION).
5. If an internal review is not required, the SDRL is distributed (OUTPUT) (NO).
6. If an internal review is required, Data Management forwards the SDRL to Reviewer(s) (YES) (ACTION).
7. The Reviewers review the SDRL and make comments (ACTION).
8. The Reviewers forward the comments to Data Management (ACTION).
9. Data Management determines whether further review is required (DECISION).
10. If no further review is required, the SDRL is distributed (OUTPUT).

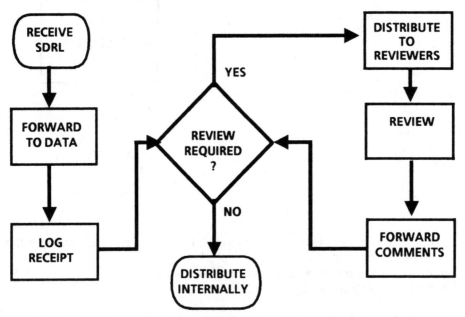

Fig. 7-5. Detailed process diagram example. SDRL, subcontractor data requirement list.

Input/output analysis

Input/output analysis is a technique for identifying any interdependency problems of a process. This identification is done by defining the process and listing inputs and outputs. Once the inputs and outputs are determined, the relationship of inputs to outputs is analyzed, along with the roles of the organization. Figure 7-6 shows the inputs to and outputs from the logistics process.

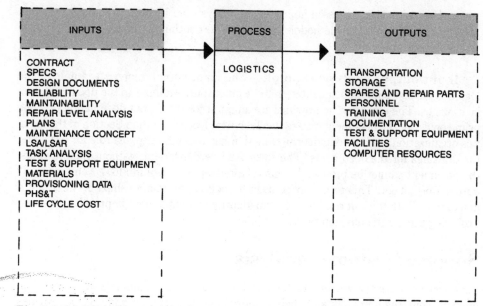

Fig. 7-6. Logistics process inputs and outputs. LSA, logistics support analysis; LSAR, logistics support analysis, record; PHS&T, packing, handling, storage and transportation.

Input analysis

Inputs   List the inputs of the process.
Needs   Define the requirements and roles of the organization.
Process   Determine what the job is.
Understanding   State prime and support responsibilities.
Thoroughness   Do a complete analysis of all inputs.

Output analysis

Output   List the output of the process.
Understanding   State prime and support responsibilities.
Talk   Communicate with suppliers, owner, and customers.
Process   Determine what the process is.
Understanding   Listen to the customer.
Thoroughness   Do a complete analysis of the output.

Input/output analysis steps   The steps for an input/output analysis are as follows:

1. Define the actual process.
2. List the inputs and outputs of the process.
3. Determine prime (owner) and support (influencing) responsibilities.
4. Match inputs and outputs with functions or organizations.
5. Define the roles of the functions or organizations.

6. Document the results on input/output analysis work sheet.
7. Use improvement methodology within the continuous improvement cycle to improve the process.

Input/output analysis example   The input/output analysis example of the logistics process shows documentation to be an output. An input to the documentation is drawings. The engineering drawings are an input for the output documentation. The prime owner of the documentation is the Technical Documentation Section of the logistics organization, and the engineering function has the main support role for providing the drawings for the documents. The roles are interdependent; without the drawings, the document cannot be produced. This relationship is shown in FIG. 7-7 on the input/output work sheet. This form can be used to look at the relationships between input and output. With this information, you can identify and implement improved opportunities using the continuous improvement cycle.

Supplier/customer analysis

Supplier/customer analysis is a technique that involves your suppliers in the development of your requirements and their conformance to them. In addition, it provides insight into your customer's needs and expectations and the ways you can meet those expectations.

It is important to develop a partnership with your suppliers and a relationship with the customers you want to keep. Use surveys and interviews to ensure mutual agreement on supplier requirements and customer expectations. A supplier/customer analysis work sheet can be used to document results. Always communicate, listen, and thoroughly analyze supplier and customer perceptions in order to improve continuously supplier performance, the process, and customer satisfaction.

Supplier analysis

Survey   Do you survey suppliers to ensure that requirements are known?
Understanding   Is there a mutual understanding of requirements?
Partnership   Do you have an established partnership with key suppliers?
Perceptions   What are suppliers' perceptions of your requirements?
Listening   Do you listen to suppliers' concerns? Do suppliers listen to your concerns?
Interviews   Do you conduct interviews to determine supplier perceptions?
Expectations   Are customer expectations translated into supplier requirements?
Requirements   Are your suppliers satisfying your requirements?

Customer analysis

Communication   Are you communicating to ensure that you are satisfying customers?
Understanding   Do you understand customer's needs and expectations?
Survey   Have you conducted a survey to determine whether you are satisfying your customers?

PROCESS	INPUT	OUTPUT	PRIME	SUPPORT	ROLE
Logistics	Drawings	Document	Tech.Doc.	Eng.	Inter-dependent

Fig. 7-7. Input/output work sheet.

Thoroughness   Have you completed a thorough analysis to ensure that the focus is on customer needs and expectations?

Owner   Does the owner understand the impact of the process on the customer?

Measurement   Are process outputs measured in relation to customer expectations?

Expectations   Are you satisfying mutually agreed upon customer expectations?
Relationship   Have you developed a relationship with key customers?

Supplier/customer analysis steps   The supplier/customer analysis steps are:

1. Identify the customer or customers, both internal and external, of the process.
2. Determine the needs and expectations of your customer.
3. Identify the products or services you provide to meet these needs and expectations.
4. Develop measures of your output that reflect customer expectations.
5. Determine whether customer expectations have been met.
6. Determine who owns or influences the product or service.
7. Identify your principal inputs (manpower, material, machine, method, environment).
8. Determine whether suppliers know their requirements and their impact on your success at meeting customer expectations.
9. Involve your suppliers in the development of your requirements and their conformance to them.
10. Identify suppliers that are not meeting requirements.
11. Document results on supplier/customer analysis work sheet.
12. Use structured improvement methodology to improve supplier performance, the process, and customer satisfaction.

Supplier/customer analysis example   This supplier/customer analysis example also uses the engineering drawings required for documentation used in the input/output analysis. First, transfer the input, output, and supplier information from the input/output work sheet to the supplier/customer work sheet, as shown in FIG. 7-8. Second, determine customer expectations for a usable document. This is accomplished by communication with the customer, that is, maintenance personnel. Third, determine a specific measurement. In this case, the customer expects the document to be 100 percent accurate, Fourth, measure performance. Fifth, determine whether the document is meeting customer expectations.

To complete the supplier side of the equation, the engineering function must be informed of the drawings' impact on providing an accurate document to the maintenance personnel. The requirement for complete and accurate drawings must be measured to determine whether engineering is meeting requirements.

All the information from the supplier/customer work sheet is used within the improvement methodology to improve supplier performance, the process, and customer satisfaction.

Key points

- Benchmarking provides a best target measurement.
- Benchmark the process as well as the performance goal.
- Process understanding is improved through process diagraming.
- Process diagram only to the desired level.

INPUT	SUPPLIER	REQUIREMENT	MET/ NOT	OUTPUT	CUSTOMER	EXPECTATION	MET/ NOT
Drawings	Eng.	complete and accurate		Document	Maintenance personnel	100% accurate	

Fig. 7-8. Supplier/customer work sheet.

- Keep the process diagram within specified boundaries, but be as thorough as possible.
- The relationship between inputs and outputs affects customer satisfaction.
- Develop a partnership with your suppliers and a relationship with the customers and constantly analyze these relationships.
- Listening is most critical during supplier/customer analysis.

8

Selection
tools and techniques

*Security against defeat implies defensive tactics; ability to
defeat means taking the offensive.*

Sun Tzu
Art of War

During the improvement methodology, often selections from several options must be made. Therefore, a method for selection is necessary in order to focus on the best alternative. Some of the most common selection methods used are voting, the selection matrix, and the selection grid. These selection tools and techniques all assist a group in arriving at a decision through concensus. Although a decision can be made by vote of the majority or decision of a leader or management, concensus is the best process to use for selection.

Selection techniques are used to help clarify assumptions and focus on consensus. Some of the elements of selection are as follows:

Select a technique.
Establish criteria.
List problems, opportunities, or alternatives.
Evaluate problems or opportunities using criteria.
Communicate.
Trade off.
Involve everyone.
Obtain a consensus.
Need the selection to solve the problem, take advantage of the opportunity, or implement the solution.

Selection techniques steps

The steps of the techniques used to select a problem, opportunity, or alternative are:

1. List problems, opportunities, or alternatives.
2. Determine criteria.
3. Select method (voting, matrix, or grid).
4. Make a decision.

Selection techniques criteria

Although the team, the main organizational structure for accomplishing critical missions, can select any criteria, the criteria below provide examples for consideration.

Cost
Resources
Importance
Time
Effect
Risk
Integration with organization's objectives
Authority

Voting

Voting is a selection technique used to determine majority opinion. This technique can be useful in narrowing a list of problems, opportunities, or alternatives. Since this method often leads to a win/lose situation, it is not recommended as a final decision-making technique for selecting a problem/opportunity or solution. All selection techniques focus on reaching a consensus on a win/win solution. The two primary voting techniques are rank order voting and multivoting.

Rank order voting

Rank order voting is a quick method for ranking a list of problems, opportunities, or alternatives to determine the top priorities.

Rank order voting steps   The steps in rank order voting are as follows:

1. Generate a list of items requiring a decision.
2. Combine similar items.
3. Number the items.
4. Have each member of the team rate each item on a scale of one to five, with five being the highest number.
5. Total the points for each item.
6. Rank the items from highest to lowest according to the total number of points.
7. Reach a consensus on the top priority.

Multivoting

Multivoting is a technique used to reduce a large list of problems, opportunities, or alternatives to a smaller number of items. Typically, during the understanding stage of improvement methodology, a team has a large list of concerns with the process. The team must reduce this list to find a consensus on the most critical issues.

Multivoting steps   The steps in multivoting are as follows:

1. Generate a list of items requiring a decision.
2. Combine similar items.
3. Number the items.
4. Have each member select some of the items from the list. This is accomplished by each person writing the number of the items on separate paper. For instance, if the total number of items on the list is 50, the items are numbered 1 to 50. Each person then is asked to select, for example, the top 20 items from the list of 50.
5. Total the number of votes for each item.
6. Create a new list of items of the top 20 vote getters. Number the items 1 through 20.
7. Have each member select a lower number of items from the list. For instance, from the list of 20 items, each member selects, for example, the top 5 items.
8. Eventually reach a consensus on the top priority.

Selection matrix

A selection matrix is a technique for rating problems, opportunities, or alternatives according to specific criteria selected by the team. The problems, opportunities, or alternatives are listed on the left side of the matrix, the criteria are placed along the top. Members individually rate the problems, opportunities, or alternatives, and then determine the group ratings. This process helps to clarify assumptions and arrive at a consensus.

Selection matrix steps

The selection matrix steps are as follows:

1. The problems, opportunities, or alternatives are listed on the left side of the matrix.
2. The team selects the criteria to be considered in evaluating the problems, opportunities, or alternatives.
3. The criteria are listed at the top of the matrix.
4. The members individually rate the problems, opportunities, or alternatives.
5. Discussion of the problems, opportunities, or alternatives ensues.
6. The group tries to reach a consensus.

Selection matrix example

In this example, the organization's goal is to select a method of training that will ensure that test technicians can perform a certain test. Figure 8-1 shows the selection matrix. The opportunities, listed in the right-hand column, are training that is in a classroom, on-the-job, a combination of both, or none. The criteria are listed across the top. For this example, the criteria selected are effect, cost, and time to implement. Each person rates opportunities against the criteria, and the total number of points is added. Once all members' ratings are known, the group focuses on consensus.

OPPORTUNITIES ALTERNATIVES	EFFECT A LOT-10 LITTLE-1	COST LITTLE-10 A LOT-1	TIME LITTLE-10 A LOT-1	TOTAL
Formal classroom	8	6	3	17
On-the-job	4	8	7	19
Combination of both	9	7	6	22
None	1	7	10	18

Fig. 8-1. Selection matrix.

Selection grid

A selection grid compares each problem, opportunity, or alternative against others using the criteria chosen by the group.

Selection grid steps

1. List problems, opportunities, or alternatives.
2. Determine criteria.
3. Compare each pair of problems, opportunities, or alternatives against others using criteria.
4. Try to reach a consensus.

Selection grid example

In this example, the team or organization must select a truck to deliver parts to another facility. Figure 8-2 shows the selection grid. The choices are TRUCK1, TRUCK2,

~~TRUCK1~~	TRUCK1	~~TRUCK1~~
TRUCK2	~~TRUCK3~~	TRUCK4
	TRUCK2	~~TRUCK2~~
	~~TRUCK3~~	TRUCK4
		~~TRUCK3~~
		TRUCK4

Totals

TRUCK1	1
TRUCK2	2
TRUCK3	0
TRUCK4	3

Fig. 8-2. Selection grid.

TRUCK3, or TRUCK4. Each choice is compared against every other choice by each member of the group. Figure 8-2 is one person's grid and his or her total count. The person considers TRUCK1 and TRUCK2 using his or her criteria and crosses off TRUCK1. He or she then compares TRUCK1 and TRUCK3 and crosses off one, and so on. The total number of each selection not crossed off is counted. The highest number is the initial choice, in the example, TRUCK 4. The team then discusses all these choices. From this process, assumptions are clarified and a consensus can be reached.

Decision making

The decision-making process is the process of making the selection. In making a decision, the impact and support of the outcome should be considered. A group will be more committed to success if the decision is reached by consensus. Therefore, consensus should be used when selecting a problem/opportunity to address or a solution to implement. Further, the selection should have a win/win outcome. Decisions reached by any method other than consensus result in a win/lose situation, and win/lose decision results in lack of total commitment and support for the selection.

Although consensus is the recommended method for group decision making, other methods also exist. They include the following:

- Decision by majority. This is a decision by more than half of the representatives.
- Decision by a leader. In some cases, the leader makes the decision.
- Decision by management. Management can make the decision.

Consensus

Consensus means everyone in the group accepts and supports a decision. Consensus equals commitment. It is critical when selecting a process to improve, a problem to solve, a mission to accomplish, an opportunity to pursue, a recommendation to follow, or a solution to implement. Consensus requires an understanding of the process, the mission, the problem, and all the possible alternatives. Further, discussion of all the possible driving and restraining forces, causes and effects, and process interactions from all the viewpoints of the group is absolutely essential. Once understanding is gained and discussion takes place, the group can proceed with the process of arriving at a consensus.

Decision by the Majority or the Leader

In many cases during group activities, decisions may be made by the majority of the membership or by the leader. Decisions made by the majority or the leader are usually reserved for relatively minor aspects of group activities, such as the decision to use a specific tool or technique. In all cases the particular method of decision making should be determined by the group.

Decision by management

Management can make the decision; decisions by management are necessary. However, in a TQM environment, management should always be aware of the impact of decisions on the TQM environment. As with consensus, decisions by management accompanied by understanding and discussion frequently result in support for even unpopular decisions.

Key points

- Selection techniques help to clarify assumptions and focus on consensus.
- Consensus is important when selecting an opportunity or alternative.
- Consensus means everyone understands and supports the decision.
- The criteria and method selected are critical to the desired outcome.
- All decisions should focus on a win/win outcome that is the best for the whole organization.

9

Analysis
tools and techniques

*If you know the enemy and know yourself, your victory will not
stand in doubt; if you know Heaven and know Earth, you may make
your victory complete.*

Sun Tzu
Art of War

During the improvement methodology, thorough analysis is extremely important. The
tools and techniques for analysis help improve the process, determine underlying
causes of the problem, identify the vital few, and describe both sides of an issue. Total
Quality Management analysis tools and techniques are process analysis, cause-and-
effect analysis, data/statistical analysis, and force field analysis.

Process analysis

Process analysis is a tool used to improve a process and reduce process time by eliminating non-value-added activities and/or by simplifying the process. In process analysis
you must first eliminate non-value-added processes, activities, and tasks. Once this is
done, process simplification is next. These initial actions achieve quick results at little
or no cost.

Process analysis steps

1. Construct a top-down or detailed process diagram (chapter 7).
2. Ensure that waits between processes/activities are identified.
3. Determine the time and cost of each process/activity and time of waits.
4. Reduce or eliminate waits.

5. Select critical activities (high time or high cost).
6. Eliminate non-value-added processes/activities.
7. Eliminate parts of the process.
8. Simplify value-added processes/activities. During this step, attempt to combine processes/activities, change the amount of time or frequency, do processes/ activities in parallel with another process, and use another method to do the process.
9. Use continuous improvement methodology to further improve the process.

Cause-and-effect analysis

Cause-and-effect analysis is a useful technique for helping a group examine the underlying causes. Figure 9-1 shows a cause-and-effect diagram. The application of this technique usually results in a more specific definition of the problem. An added benefit is that it is graphically clear; this helps members see patterns and relationships among potential causes. This type of analysis lets individual members express their interpretation of the problem and frequently it stimulates further brainstorming and clarification of the problem.

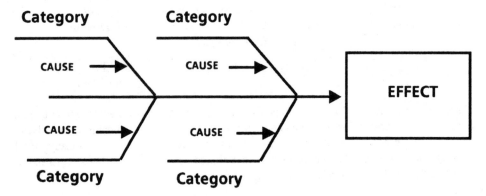

Fig. 9-1. Cause-and-effect diagram.

Cause-and-effect example

Figure 9-2 shows the cause-and-effect diagram for the example. The steps of the cause-and-effect example are described in the following paragraphs.

Cause-and-effect analysis steps

Step 1   Define the problem.

The team is asked to identify the problem, and the problem is the effect. In the example, the problem is a piece of equipment with mean time between failure (MTBF) of 400 hours. This MTBF is too low. Thus, the MTBF is the problem, or effect.

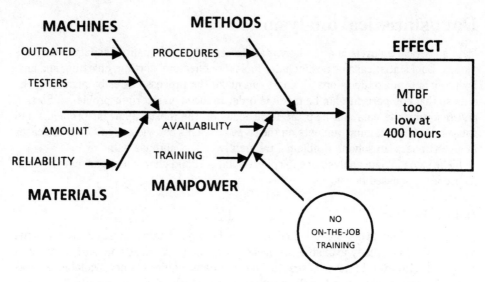

Fig. 9-2. Cause-and-effect example. MTBF, mean time between failure.

Step 2   Define the major categories.

Next, the major categories of possible causes of the problem are identified. The most popular categories are machines, methods, materials, and manpower. The team must tailor these categories to the specific problem, and you are not limited to these categories. Other categories might be environment, culture, and so on. For this example, however, machines, methods, materials, and manpower categories were selected.

Step 3   Brainstorm possible causes.

Having identified the categories, the team then brainstorms possible causes. List possible causes under the appropriate category. The brainstorming rules described in chapter 6 apply in this step. It is sometimes helpful for the leader to keep repeating the heading for the cause in relation to the effect. For instance: under manpower, what is a cause of low MTBF? In addition, the leader must build on people's ideas in the search for underlying causes for the problem.

Step 4   Identify the most likely causes.

The group looks for clues to the most likely causes. Once all the causes are examined, the group selected the most likely cause by using the selection techniques from chapter 8.

Step 5   Verify the most likely cause.

The most likely cause is verified by measuring, by means of a test, collecting more data on the problem, or communicating with customers to verify or reject the cause. Once your group has identified the cause, you can begin to generate alternative solutions and work to solve the problem.

Data/statistical analysis

Data statistical analysis is a fundamental element of Total Quality Management techniques. Data statistical analysis includes tools for collecting, sorting, charting, and analyzing data to make decisions. A chart can make the process easier by arranging the data so that comparisons can be made in order to focus on the right problems. Sorting and resorting the data can help the team focus on the most important problems and causes. Even small improvements on the right problems can yield significant increases in effectiveness. In solving problems, frequently collect and use data.

The steps in data analysis are to collect data, sort and chart data, and analyze data. These are discussed below.

Data collection

The first step in data collection is to determine the type of data needed. Sometimes the data required is already available. In these cases, the team must only sort, chart, and analyze it. However, in many cases, the specific data required is not available. At this point, determine what data to collect, where to collect the data, and how to collect it.

The credibility of the data corresponds to the complexity of the data collection method. Usually the more complex the collection method, the greater the chance for incorrect data.

Check sheets A data collection chart must sometimes be designed to simplify data collection. An example of an easy-to-use check sheet to collect the data is shown in FIG. 9-3. This check sheet shows the discrepancies encountered in a part over a 3-week

DISCREPANCY	WEEK 1	WEEK 2	WEEK 3	TOTAL
BOARD	///	/	//	6
SOLDER	/	/		2
WIRING	/////	///	////	12
CONNECTOR	/////	/////	/////	15
COMPONENT	///// ///// ///// //	///// ///// /////	///// ///// ///	45
TOTAL	31	25	24	80

Fig. 9-3. Data collection chart: a check sheet.

period. As a discrepancy is encountered, the faulty item is checked. For instance, as shown at the bottom of the chart, in the first week, 17 discrepancies in the part were attributed to a faulty component. In the second week, 15 discrepancies in the part were attributed to a faulty component; and in the third week, 13.

Check sheets can help a team systematically collect the data. Make sure that the data is unbiased, accurate, properly recorded, and representative of typical conditions. Data come from many sources. Frequently, data already exists but has not been analyzed.

Sampling   In data collection, it is often impractical to check 100 percent of the items, that is, the entire population of the data. A sample of the whole population can be all that is required. It can yield reliable information. A sampling table can help you determine an appropriate sample size. These tables are usually available from the industrial engineering, quality, or management services departments in an organization. To reduce the chance for biased results, use a random or systematic method to select samples. A random sample allows each item an equal chance of being selected. A systematic sample selects every fifth, tenth, or twentieth item. Such sampling reduces the chance for biased results.

Data sorting and charting

Once the team has collected the data, it needs to sort the data into classes or categories. Once sorted, the data is put on a chart. Charts are pictures of the data that highlight the important trends and significant relationships. When using charts and graphs, create titles and categories for clarity. Keep them simple and report all the facts needed to be fair and accurate. Charts and graphs are very useful in data analysis and communication of data to others when gaining approval or support for an improvement.

Bar chart   A bar chart is useful when comparing many events or items. Figure 9-4 shows a bar chart of the information from the check sheet in FIG. 9-3. The bar chart shows the number of repairs by categories arranged from the highest number to the lowest number of repairs.

Pie chart   A pie chart shows the relationship between the items and the whole. Figure 9-5 shows a pie chart of the information from the check sheet in FIG. 9-3. The pie chart shows each repair item's contribution to the total percent of repairs for the item. This chart clearly shows that component repair is the most common type of repair. In this case, your organization should focus its efforts on reducing the number of failures in the components.

Line chart   Use a line chart when describing and comparing quantifiable information. A line chart provides insight into statistical trends particularly over a specified period of time. Figure 9-6 shows a line chart of the information from the check sheet in FIG. 9-3. This line chart shows the number of repairs by category per week.

Scatter chart   A scatter chart depicts the relationship between two or more factors. For instance, it might show the relationship between the number of items tested and the number of failures.

Figure 9-7 shows a series of scatter charts. The X axis of each chart is the number tested, and the Y axis is the number that failed. First, the information is plotted on the graph. Next, a line is fitted through the scatter diagram. Then, the chart is analyzed to

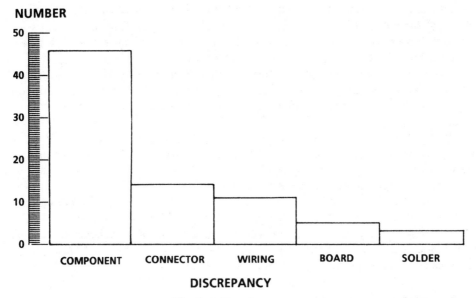

Fig. 9-4. Bar chart.

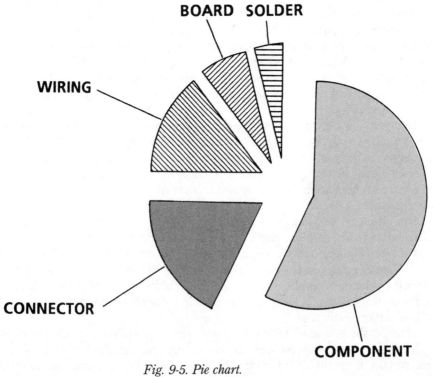

Fig. 9-5. Pie chart.

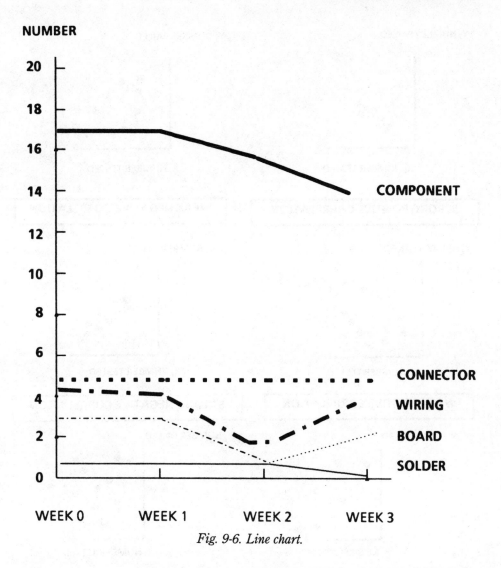

Fig. 9-6. Line chart.

determine the relationship. A positive correlation indicates a direct relationship between the factors; that is, as the number of hours that an item is used increases, the number of repairs increases. A negative correlation shows an inverse relationship; that is, as the number of hours that an item is used increases, the number of repairs decreases. The relationship could be depicted by a curve. This occurs when the number of repairs changes by some fixed proportion and is sometimes referred to as the learning curve. Finally, if no pattern is evident, no correlation exists.

   Histogram   A histogram is a vertical bar chart that shows frequency of data in column form. Figure 9-8 shows a histogram. This type of data charting is useful for identifying changes in a process. A histogram can provide insight into the performance of a process and appropriate corrective actions by means of its centering, width, and

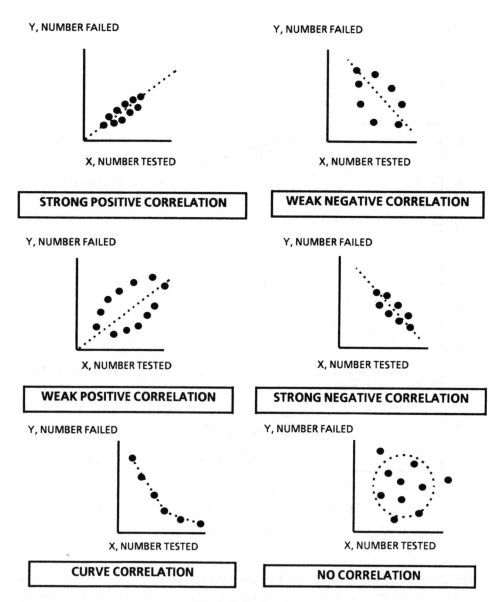

Fig. 9-7. Scatter chart.

shape. The closer the columns of the histogram to the center of the chart, the more on target the process. The wider the spread of the columns from the center, the greater the variation of the process from the target. Any change from a normal bell shape may indicate a problem area.

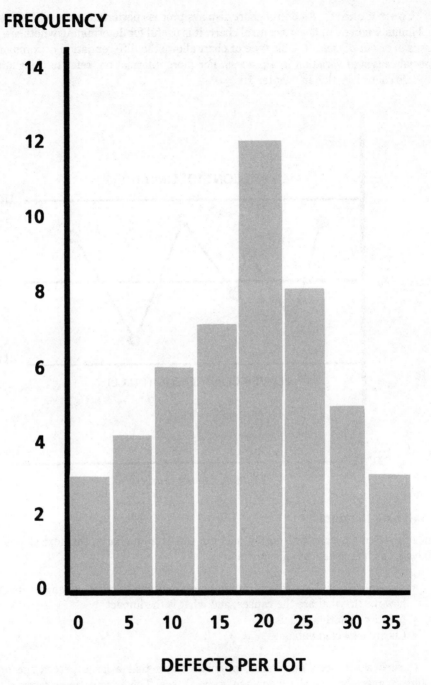

Fig. 9-8. Histogram.

Control chart   A control chart displays process performance in relation to control limits. Figure 9-9 shows a control chart. It is useful for determining whether a process is in or out of control. This type of chart allows the differentiation of common and special causes of variation in a process. For more information, refer to the statistical process control section in chapter 10.

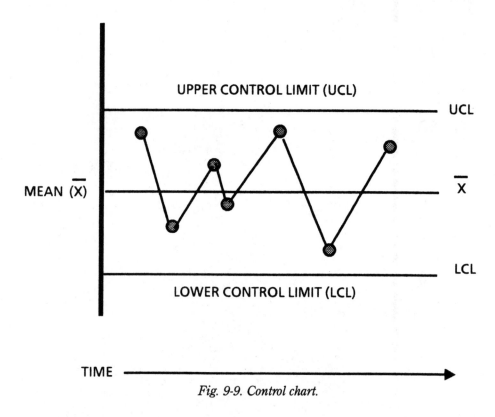

Fig. 9-9. Control chart.

Analyzing the data

Once the team has collected, sorted, and put the data on charts, the next step is data analysis, to identify the significant findings.

- Ask specific problem identification questions such as what, when, where, who, how much, what are the causes, and what is the impact?
- Identify underlying causes
- Clarify expected outcome

Pareto analysis   The Pareto principle states that a large percentage of the results is caused by a small percentage of the causes. This is sometimes referred to as the 80/20 rule. An example of this rule is "Twenty percent of the errors produces 80 percent of the scrap."

The exact percentage is not important. The importance of this rule is that it focuses on the vital few problems that produce the big results. Greater success is probable by concentrating on those vital few problems that bring major results, rather than the trivial many that provide minor results.

Figure 9-10 shows a Pareto chart. In this chart, the vital few are components and connectors. By focusing on correcting these problems, 80 percent of the repairs can be eliminated.

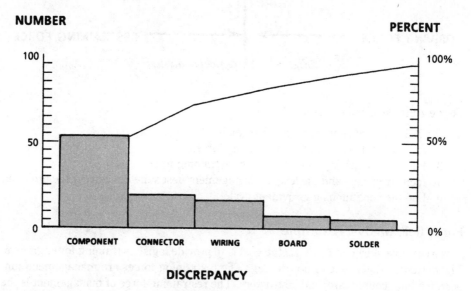

Fig. 9-10. Pareto chart.

Variability analysis   Variability exists in everything. The presence of variability is a major obstacle to quality. As stated in chapter 5 of this book, variation has common and special causes. By examining the statistical data, deviations from target values can be monitored, controlled, and improved. Variability analysis is a fundamental, essential tool of Total Quality Management.

Force field analysis

Force field analysis is a technique that helps a team describe the forces at work in a given situation. Figure 9-11 shows a force field analysis chart. The underlying assumption of the force field concept is that every situation results from a balance of forces: restraining forces and driving forces. Restraining forces are those that keep the situation from improving, whereas driving forces are those that push toward the achievement of the goal. Force field analysis "forces" the team to examine strengths, as well as problems. Sometimes by building on a driving force or strength, a team can bring about the needed improvement.

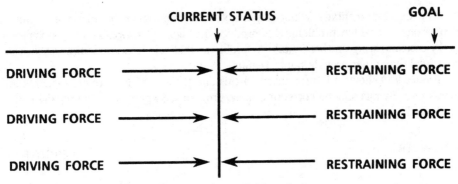

Fig. 9-11. Force field analysis.

Force field analysis steps

1. Define the current status and the goal.
2. Identify and prioritize the restraining forces.
3. Identify the driving forces for each restraining force.
4. Identify owners and the level of management best suited to correct the problem.
5. Use the continuous improvment cycle.

Force field analysis example

In the example shown in FIG. 9-12, the goal is to provide logistics training for engineers. The current status is one of no training. The restraining forces are management support, funding, courseware, and instructors. The restraining force of management is the one selected to develop driving forces. The driving forces that can be used to eliminate

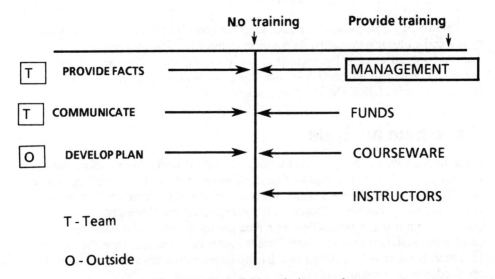

Fig. 9-12. Force field analysis example.

or weaken management's nonsupport are facts, communication, and a plan. After these conditions are established, the team can provide facts and communicate. The other alternative, to provide a plan, requires outside assistance. Finally, the team selects an alternative or alternatives.

Key points

- Analysis of process for elimination of non-value-added activities and simplification is an initial analysis step.
- Elimination of underlying causes is the main focus of cause-and-effect analysis.
- Accurate measurements are the key to effective analysis.
- The credibility of data directly relates to the complexity of the data collection method. The more complex the data collection method, the more likely the data will be incorrect.
- Use the chart that best shows correct results.
- Data collection and analysis monitor and improve the process. Never use them to control or take unfair advantage of others.
- Focus on the vital few items that provide the greater chance for payoff.

10

System improvement
tools and techniques

The general who wins a battle makes many calculations in his
temple before the battle is fought. The general who loses a
battle makes but few calculations beforehand. . . . It is by
attention to this point that I can foresee who is likely
to win or lose.

Sun Tzu
Art of War

Many times a system or process must be developed or completely redesigned to make
an improvement. System improvement focuses on the development or redesign of systems. A system can be as complicated as an F-16 fighter jet or a car, or as simple as a
flight control surface or a car door. Total Quality Management system improvement
tools and techniques can be used for any system, subsystem, or part. In fact, some of
the tools, such as statistical process control (SPC) and quality function deployment
(QFD), have been used successfully for the continuous improvement of entire organizational systems.

Since the performance of a product is critical to customer satisfaction, this chapter
focuses on the system improvement of a product. The product is any output to a customer, including a system, subsystem, or part. Product design, process design, and production processes have a major impact on product performance.

The tools and techniques described in this chapter have specific application to
product design, process design, and production processes. However, you can use these
tools and techniques to improve any system in your organization. They are applicable to
whole systems, subsystems, or parts.

System improvement

As stated, system improvement focuses on improving the actual performance of a product through product design, process design, and the planning of production processes.

System improvement starts with the customer, as shown in FIG. 10-1. Next, the product and processes are designed. The voice of the customer carries through product and process design to the actual production of the product. Within product design,

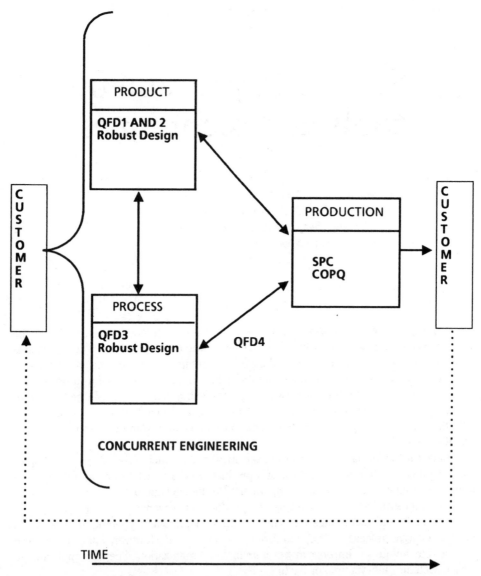

Fig. 10-1. System improvements overview. QFD, quality function deployment; SPC, statistical process control; COPQ, cost of poor quality.

process design, and production processes, specific tools are useful for ensuring customer satisfaction. These tools are concurrent engineering (CE), robust design (RD), quality functional deployment (QFD), statistical process control (SPC), and cost of poor quality (COPQ).

Concurrent engineering is useful during the product and process planning and design phases for reducing the time and cost of product development. Quality functional deployment is beneficial for carrying the voice of the customer throughout the entire process. Robust design focuses on designing in quality by eliminating loss. Statistical process control is a technique for measuring process behavior during production. Cost of poor quality emphasizes the elimination of waste in all processes.

Concurrent engineering

Concurrent engineering, like Total Quality Management, is a philosophy and a set of guiding principles in which product design and process design are developed concurrently, that is, with some overlap of product design and process development. CE includes production and support planning. Figure 10-2 shows the difference between

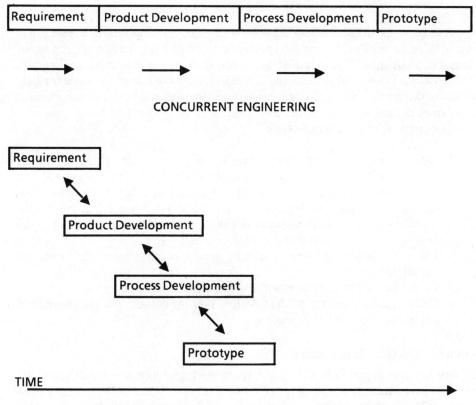

Fig. 10-2. Comparison of sequential and concurrent engineering.

sequential engineering and concurrent engineering. With sequential engineering, the engineering phases are accomplished one after the other. With CE, the engineering phases overlap.

Concurrent engineering is a subsystem of Total Quality Management that focuses on system and parametric design. Refer to robust design phases in this chapter for more detail. Like TQM, concurrent engineering requires a management and cultural environment, teams, and an improvement system that focuses on customer satisfaction.

The concurrent engineering philosophy includes:

Customer focus
Organization-wide, systematic approach
Never-ending improvements: product, process, production
Concurrent design of product and related processes
Upper-management leadership
Robust design
Reduced cost and time, improved quality and productivity
Engineering planning initiatives, including automation
New reliance on multifunctional teams
Tools and techniques such as quality function deployment, design of experiments,
    Taguchi approach, statistical process control

A more formal definition from the Institute for Defense Analysis, in Report R-338, states, "Concurrent Engineering is a systematic approach to the integrated, concurrent design of products and their related processes, including manufacture and support. This approach is intended to cause the developers, from the outset, to consider all elements of the product life cycle from conception, through disposal, including quality, cost, schedule, and user requirements."

Concurrent engineering steps

1. Establish a multifunction team. Have representation from all required disciplines. The team should include representatives from such functions as systems/design engineering, reliability and maintainability engineering, test engineering, manufacturing engineering, production engineering, purchasing, manufacturing test and assembly, logistics engineering, supportability engineering, marketing, and finance and accounting.
2. Use a systematic, disciplined, specific approach using appropriate tools and techniques.
3. Determine customer requirements. Communicate with customers.
4. Develop simultaneously product design, process design, and the planning of production and support processes.

Quality function deployment

Quality function deployment (QFD) is a disciplined approach for transforming customer requirements, or the voice of the customer, into product development requirements. QFD is a tool for making plans visible and then determining the impact of the plans. QFD involves all activities of everyone at all stages, from development through production, with a customer focus.

Figure 10-3 shows the four phases of QFD. These phases are:

1. Product planning
2. Parts deployment
3. Process planning
4. Production planning

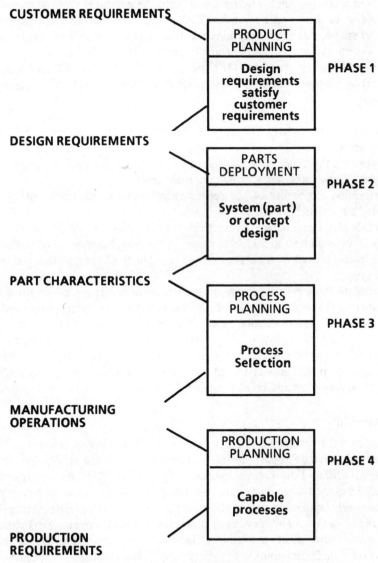

Fig. 10-3. *Quality function deployment phases overview.*

The output from each phase is the input for the next. During phase 1, customer requirements are transformed into design requirements. The steps of this phase are discussed below. In phase 2, design requirements are converted into a system (part) or concept design. Phase 3 examines candidate processes and selects one. Phase 4 involves making capable production processes.

QFD house of quality   The results of QFD planning are included on a chart called the House of Quality. The basic House of Quality planning chart, which is for phase 1 of QFD, is shown in FIG. 10-4. From this chart many other useful charts can be generated to progress from general customer requirements to specific production processes. The number and kinds of charts vary with the complexity of the project. QFD can be applied to the complete product, the system, the subsystem, and/or specific parts. At all stages of QFD application, prioritization ensures that the overall analysis does not become excessively burdensome in terms of time and cost.

House of Quality steps for QFD phase 1   To change customer requirements into production planning, the first phase of QFD, as shown in FIG. 10-4, entails the following steps:

1. Determine the whats. These are the voice of the customer, or customer demands.
2. Transform the whats or hows. These hows become the product design requirements, or characteristics, which are measurable.
3. Determine the nature of the relationships between the whats and the hows using a relationship matrix.
4. Decide how much data, which provides target values for design requirements.
5. Correlate each how to each other how, in the correlation section, or the roof of the houselike matrix. This step is used to aid in conflict resolution and trade-off analysis.
6. Complete the two competitive evaluation sections. These competitive evaluations rate the product under question against similar products produced by the competition. One evaluation relates the product features to customer satisfaction, and the other evaluation assesses the product on technical merit.
7. Assign or calculate importance ratings to help prioritize analysis efforts.
8. Analyze results. This step includes a "checks-and-balances" procedure to identify planning gaps and point to wasteful activities.

Robust design

Robust design is the design of a product for minimal quality losses. Several methodologies are associated with robust design, the major ones being traditional design of experiments (DOE) and the Taguchi approach. Traditional design of experiments is an experimental tool used to establish both parametric relationships and a product/process model in the early (applied research) stages of the design process. However, traditional design of experiments can be very costly particularly when there are many parameters and their interactional effects to examine. Traditional DOE examines various causes of performance for their contribution to variation, with the emphasis on discovering the most influential causes of variation. Traditional design of experiments can be a useful

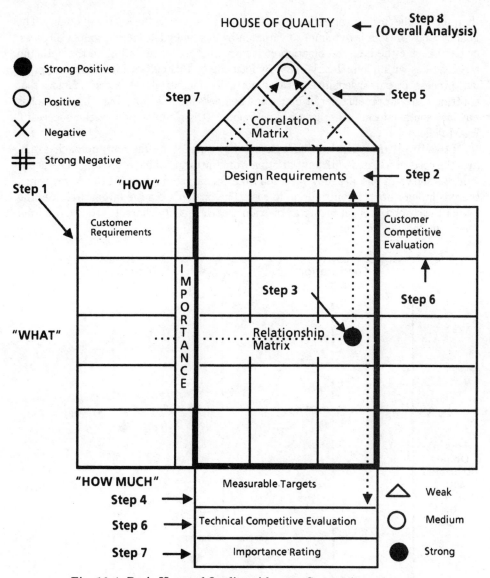

Fig. 10-4. Basic House of Quality with steps. See text for explanation.

tool in the preliminary design stage for modeling, parameter determination, research, and establishing a general understanding of product phenomena.

The other major approach to robust design is the Taguchi approach. This approach focuses on quality optimization, which is based on Dr. Taguchi's definition of quality. Taguchi, in his book *Introduction to Quality Engineering*, states, "Quality is the (measure of degree of) loss a product causes after being shipped, other than any losses caused by its intrinsic functions." Simply put, any failure to satisfy the customer is a loss. Loss is determined by variation of performance from optimum target values. Loss, therefore, in the form of variability from best target values, is the enemy of quality. The goal of robust design is to minimize variation by designing a system (product, process, or part) having the best combination of factors, that is, by centering on the optimum target values with minimal variability. By focusing on this bullseye, we make the product, process, or part insensitive to those normally uncontrollable "noise" factors that contribute to poor product performance and business failures. The Taguchi approach is not just another form of design of experiments. It is a major part of the successful TQM philosophy.

Loss function   The loss function, a key element of the Taguchi approach, examines the costs associated with any variation from the target value of a quality characteristic. As shown in FIG. 10-5, any variation from the target is a loss. At the target value, there is little or no loss contribution to cost. The farther from the target, however, the higher the costs. Costs get higher as the values of the quality characteristics move from "best" to "better" to "poor."

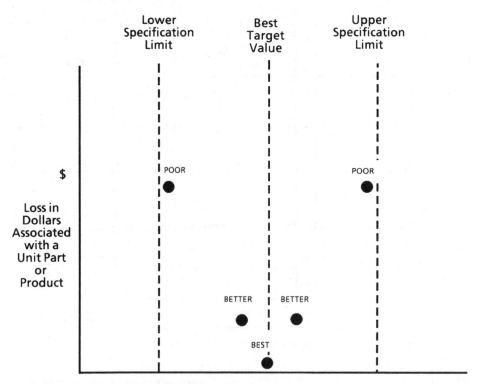

Fig. 10-5. Overview of a loss function for a "nominal-is-best" quality characteristic.

Robust design phases   Figure 10-6 depicts the design of a product or process using the Taguchi approach. A product or process design has three phases:

Phase 1   System (part) or concept design

PRODUCT   **PROCESS**

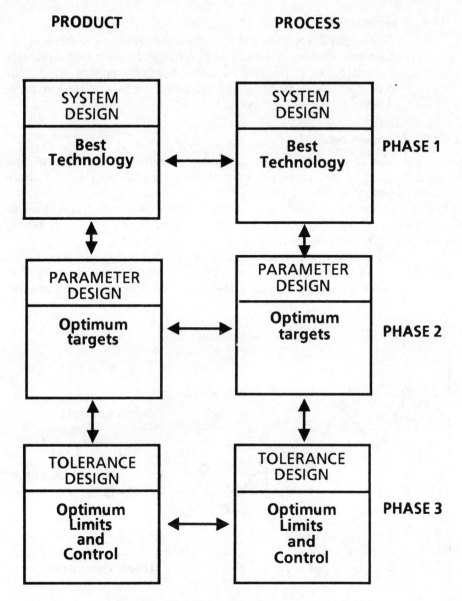

Fig. 10-6. Robust design phases.

This phase selects the design architecture (size, shape, materials, number of parts) by looking at the best available technology.

Phase 2 Parameter (or robust) design

This stage focuses on making the product performance (or process output) insensitive to variation by moving toward the best target values of quality characteristics.

Phase 3   Tolerance design

This stage focuses on setting tight tolerances to reduce variation in performance. Because this phase is the source of most added costs, it is essential to reduce the need for setting tight tolerances by successfully producing robust produces and processes in phase 2, the parameter design phase.

Statistical process control

Statistical process control (SPC) is a statistical tool for monitoring and controlling a process. SPC monitors the variation in a process with the goal being to produce the product at its best target values.

Figure 10-7 shows the major elements of statistical process control. These elements are a process chart consisting of data plots, upper control limit (UCL), lower control limit (LCL), and the mean for the process.

Figure 10-7 also illustrates variation in a process. Variation is the result of both common and special/assignable causes. Common causes produce normal variation in an established process, whereas special/assignable causes are abnormal causes of variation.

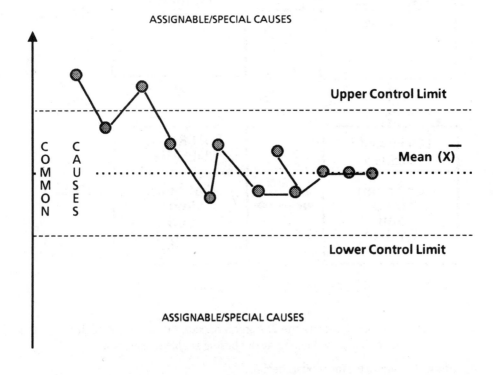

Fig. 10-7. Elements of statistical process control.

Statistical process control steps   SPC has four steps;

1. Measure the process. Ensure that data collection is thorough, complete, and accurate.
2. Bring the process under statistical control. Eliminate special/assignable causes.
3. Monitor the process; keep the process under statistical control.
4. Improve the process by seeking the best target value.

Cost of poor quality

Cost of quality is a system that provides managers with cost details that are often hidden. Cost of quality includes both the cost of conformance to quality requirements and the cost of nonconformance. Cost of conformance consists of all costs associated with maintaining acceptable quality. The cost of nonconformance, or the cost of poor quality, is the total cost incurred as a result of failure to achieve quality. Historically, organizations looked at all costs of quality. Today, many excellent organizations concentrate strictly on nonconformance costs. This approach highlights the waste, or losses, due to deviation from best target values. Once these costs are determined, they can be reduced or eliminated through the application of the continuous improvement philosophy.

Typically, the cost of nonconformance includes such items as inspection, warranty, litigation, scrap, rejects, rework, testing, retesting, change orders, errors, lengthy cycle times, inventory, and customer complaints.

Key points

- System performance has a great impact on customer satisfaction.
- The best opportunity for system performance improvements is during the product design, process design, and production planning processes.
- The earlier in the design process the change occurs, the less costly.
- Concurrent engineering, like TQM, requires a transformation from traditional methods of product and process design.
- Multifunctional teams are the key element of concurrent engineering.
- Quality function deployment is the optimal planning tool for turning customer requirements into a product and/or service that satisfies the customer.
- All products should be designed with minimum losses.
- Variation is the enemy of quality; it must be eliminated during all processes.
- Always strive to achieve the best target value, rather than merely staying within specifications.
- Parameter design is an important phase for minimizing losses due to variation from target.
- All costs of nonconformance to quality should be identified and minimized.
- Not only should processes be under control, they should perform as close as possible to the best target.
- Continuously improve all processes, beginning with processes having the highest losses associated with them.

Part IV

The Final Campaign

11

The final campaign

*When in difficult country, do not encamp. In country where high
roads intersect, join hands with your allies. Do not linger in
dangerously isolated positions. In hemmed-in situations, you must
resort to stratagem. In desperate position, you must fight.*

Sun Tzu
Art of War

The world is engaged in an economic war. An economic war and a military war have
both differences and similarities. The major difference between the two is that a military war ultimately has a victor, whereas an economic war never ends. An economic
war requires the continuous achievement of victories.

The similarities of an economic war to a military war are greater than the differences. First, an economic war is just as serious as a military war. As in a military war,
the survival of nations is at stake. There are many casualties and much destruction.
The loss of economic power by a nation results in an increase in unemployment, home-
lessness, divorce, crime, and even suicide. Major destruction of the infrastructure of a
country is devastating. Economic defeat is felt by many future generations.

An economic war is always in the final campaign. In order to achieve victories in
this, the final campaign, many changes from traditional methods are required. Many
constantly changing factors can contribute to victories at any one time. This requires
the continuous reexamining and revamping of an organization's systems and processes.

In addition to providing the philosophy and set of guiding principles for achieving
victory, TQM suggests an overall mission, objective, and strategy and the necessary
tactics, operations, and weapon systems.

As shown in FIG. 11-1, the mission is to achieve victory, and customer satisfaction is
the objective. Customer satisfaction requires a strategy of flexible, rapid response.
This strategy is enhanced through the tactic of providing both the highest quality possible and service at an optimal life cycle cost. Further, the operations focus on victory

Fig. 11-1. Objective, strategy, tactics, and operations for victory.

through actions that continuously improve systems and processes, involve people, and minimize loss.

To achieve victories, each organization and individual using the Total Quality Management philosophy and guiding principles must determine the specific changes required for his or her specific theater of operation. The victors continuously analyze themselves, the enemy, and the environment to make changes as necessary within the overall strategy, tactics, and operations to win the current battles for customer satisfaction, while creating new customers and maintaining total customer satisfaction over the long term for victory.

The TQM campaign

Remember, in an economic war, the focus must be on the mission and objective; specific strategy and tactics must be determined and carried out; operations must be conducted; weapon systems must be used. These must be constantly evaluated and changed as necessary to achieve victory.

Mission

The mission is to achieve victory or a series of victories. This is the specific reason for the existence of the organization. Again, this is the vision of the organization. Although each organization defines, determines, and redefines victory differently, all organizations must focus on their specific mission to achieve victories.

Objective

The objective of any organization is total customer satisfaction. To obtain this objective requires a Total Quality Management approach. A TQM environment and continuous improvement system focused on total customer satisfaction are essential. This requires vision and leadership, involvement of everyone and everything, continuous improvement, training and education, ownership, reward and recognition, and years of commitment and support—all aimed at total customer satisfaction.

Strategy

The strategy is flexible, rapid response. This strategy requires maximum support to achieve customer satisfaction. The organization must be capable of providing whatever the customer needs and expects at the moment it is required. To do this, the organization must thoroughly understand all processes in all of its systems. Systems and processes must be able to adapt quickly to whatever satisfies the customer.

Tactics

The tactics stress the necessity to provide the highest quality and service to achieve customer satisfaction at an optimal life cycle cost. Optimal life cycle cost comprises all the costs associated with fulfilling customer quality and service requirements. This includes the costs to the organization and the cost to the customer. Customer quality and service requirements over the entire life cycle from concept to acquisition to disposal must be considered, in other words, all the costs from "cradle to the grave."

Besides optimal life cycle cost, the tactics involve providing the highest quality and service required for customer satisfaction. Continuous planning, analysis, and actions geared to maximizing customer satisfaction are the keys to ensuring the required customer quality and service.

Operations

The operations require actions to improve systems and processes, involve people, and minimize loss on a continual basis. The organization must use the continuous improvement system, improvement methodology, and TQM tools and techniques.

Weapon systems

Many weapon systems can be used in this economic war. Some of the major weapon systems have been included in the tools and techniques chapters in this book. In addition, numerous other weapon systems are available to strive for victories. Some of the more common include: just-in-time (JIT); total production maintenance (TPM); mistake proofing; total customer service (TCS); manufacturing resource planning (MRPII); computer-aided design, computer-aided engineering, and computer-aided manufacturing (CAD/CAE/CAM); computer integrated manufacturing (CIM); computer systems; information systems (IS); and total integrated logistics (TIL).

Just-in-time

Just-in-time (JIT) is a method of having the right material just in time to be used in an operation. JIT reduces inventory and allows the immediate correction of defects. This weapon system reduces waste, decreases costs, and prevents errors.

Total production maintenance

Total production maintenance (TPM) is a system for involving the entire organization in maintenance activities. TPM involves focusing all Total Quality Management philosophy and guiding principles specifically on equipment maintenance. TPM emphasizes the involvement of everyone and everything, continuous improvement, training, optimal life cycle cost, prevention of defects, and quality design. This weapon system is effective for improving all production maintenance activities.

Mistake proofing

Mistake proofing, or poka-yoke, is a weapon for avoiding simple human error at work. Because mistake proofing frees workers from concentrating on simple tasks and allows them more time for process improvement activities, it is a major weapon in the prevention of defects.

Total customer service

Total customer service (TCS) is defined as "all features, acts, and information that augment the customer's ability to realize the potential value of a core product or service." TCS is so defined in the book *Total Customer Service* by William H. Davidow and Bro Uttal. This weapon system focuses on service quality as one of the major contributors to customer satisfaction. This is the "ultimate weapon."

Manufacturing resource planning

Manufacturing resource planning (MRPII) is an overall system for planning and controlling a manufacturing company's operations. The MRPII weapon system is used as a management tool to monitor and control manufacturing operations.

Computer-aided design, computer-aided engineering, and computer-aided manufacturing

Computer-aided design, computer-aided engineering, and computer-aided manufacturing (CAD/CAE/CAM) are automated systems for assisting in the design, engineering, and manufacturing processes. The CAD/CAE/CAM weapon systems are used to improve systems and processes, enhance product and process design, reduce the time factor, and eliminate losses.

Computer integrated manufacturing

Computer integrated manufacturing (CIM) is the integration of computer-aided design and computer-aided manufacturing (CAD/CAM) for all design and manufacturing processes. The CIM weapon system improves on the CAD/CAM weapon system by eliminating redundancy.

Computer systems

Computer systems comprise a wide range of weapon systems such as hardware, software, firmware, robotics, expert systems, and artificial intelligence. Computer systems are a major technological weapon system in the economic war.

Information systems

Information systems (IS) are an automated TQM weapon system used to focus an organization on its vision. You can use the IS to plan, design, analyze, monitor, and respond to critical strategic information essential to achieving customer satisfaction (internal/external). An information system allows continuous review, analysis, and correction.

Total integrated logistics

Total integrated logistics (TIL) is the integration of all logistics elements involved in the inputs to the organization, the processes within the organization, and the outputs of the organization to ensure total customer supportability at an optimal life cycle cost. This weapon system aims at total customer satisfaction by supporting the operations of the organization and the customer. TIL is the secret weapon system in the economic war.

TIL is discussed in detail in the next section.

*The skillful general does not raise a second levy, neither are
his supply wagons loaded more than twice. Once war is declared,
he will not waste precious time in waiting for reinforcements,
nor will he turn his army back for fresh supplies, but crosses
the enemy's frontier without delay.*

Sun Tzu
Art of War

Total integrated logistics

Total integrated logistics (TIL) is a weapon system requiring further explanation. It is a new, innovative concept within the commercial world. Before a discussion of TIL can be given, a basic understanding of logistics is necessary.

Logistics is a process that encompasses all activities supporting a system. Logistics touches all the processes required to create, produce, and sustain a system. The system can be an organization, a product, a service, a weapon system, even a combat force. Logistics involves everything but the actual system itself.

The world's military organizations have long recognized the importance of logistics in military operations. In fact, one concept of logistics comes from the military. Logistics concerns acquiring, maintaining and transporting of military material, manpower, and facilities. Logistics has always played a major role in military operations. It has made the difference between defeat and victory in many military wars.

Logistics has only recently become important in business operations. In the business environment, logistics normally means the flow of goods and services into a firm, through the firm, and to the ultimate customer. This concept limits the impact of logistics within the business environment. In reality, logistics has a major effect on customer satisfaction. Logistics helps create and sustain customer satisfaction. This broader concept of logistics encompassing all the aspects of the business is needed for victory in the current economic war.

Logistics is necessary in both the military and business environment. It focuses the organization on customer satisfaction, whether it is meeting a readiness objective (military) or providing a service or product (business). Logistics impacts the inputs to the organization, the processes within the organization, and the outputs of the organization. Logistics ensure that the right elements are available at the right time in the right quantity. Further, logistics influences optimum product development, process design, and production. It concerns the optimal mix of customer supportability at the lowest possible life cycle cost and has a major impact on service quality. It is easy to see that logistics is a critical element in every aspect of a system.

The integration of all logistics elements into a logistics system supporting the overall organizational system provides many advantages. An integrated system provides an integrated, consistent, organization-wide focus. The U.S. military has long understood the requirement for integrated logistics support. In fact, the military has instituted Integrated Logistics Support (ILS) as the discipline and the unified management of the technical logistics disciplines that plan and develop support for the military forces. ILS is an essential part of all system acquisitions. It has the following goals:

- Support and influence design.
- Develop resource requirements.
- Acquire resources.
- Provide support for minimum cost.

The concept of integrating all aspects of logistics in a commercial enterprise is not widespread. Most commercial logistics efforts are limited to integrating the flow of goods and services into, through, and out of the enterprise. Totally integrating all the aspects of logistics has not been recognized in commercial operations.

However, total integrated logistics can become an important competitive advantage. The total integration of all logistics elements ensures that the right item is at the right place at the right time, in the right quantity, and at the right costs. It eliminates duplicate activities, reduces waste, streamlines the process, shortens cycle time, provides flexible response, and ensures customer satisfaction. In today's economic war, logistics is truly a secret weapon of the final campaign.

Total integrated logistics definition

Total integrated logistics (TIL) is the integration of all logistics elements involved in the inputs to the organization, the processes within the organization, and the outputs of the organization to ensure customer supportability at an optimal life cycle cost. TIL expands the Total Quality Management approach to the logistics processes. TIL emphasizes total, or all-encompassing, integration of all logistics elements and stresses the approach of system, that is, a focus on the entire process including all the inputs, the process itself, and the outputs to the customer. Further, customer supportability at an optimal life cycle cost is the target, as with TQM. In addition, all the philosophy and guiding principles of TQM are essential to TIL. TIL is a systematic, integrated, consistent, organization-wide logistics approach. Figure 11-2 shows the total integrated

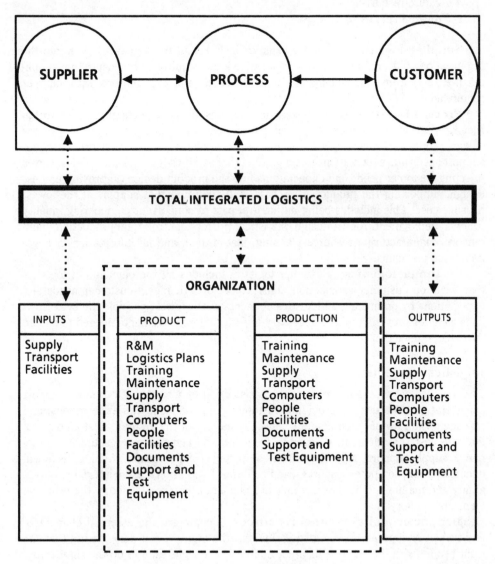

Fig. 11-2. Total integrated logistics.

logistics concept operating in a TQM environment. TIL includes supplier, process, and customer-oriented logistics. The goals of total integrated logistics are:

- Integrate all logistics aspects of the operations of the organizations to include inputs, the processes, and the outputs to optimize life cycle cost.
- Ensure customer supportability, the primary consideration throughout the process, especially during design, for total customer satisfaction.
- Develop customer supportability requirements.
- Acquire resources.
- Provide logistics services.

Supplier logistics   Supplier logistics includes all the logistics inputs into the organization. The organization must determine input requirements, ensure that suppliers meet requirements, and match customer needs and expectations with supplier requirements.

Process logistics   Process logistics includes all the aspects of logistics within the organization. These include all elements involved in product development, process design, production, and support. The goal of process logistics is to transform customer support needs and expectations into a product that satisfies the customer. This involves injecting customer needs and expectations into the product design, improving process design, supporting the production process, and acquiring that support at the lowest possible cost. This includes being an integral part of concurrent engineering, quality function deployment, robust design, statistical process control, total production maintenance, manufacturing resource planning, just-in-time, and all information management systems teams.

Customer logistics   Customer logistics includes all the elements of logistics that focus on customer satisfaction. This aspect of TIL meets customer needs and expectations by optimizing all logistics elements at the lowest possible life cycle cost. This includes providing all the necessary logistics support elements needed to ensure customer satisfaction.

Logistics elements

The logistics elements ensure customer satisfaction by integrating customer support considerations into design; providing customer support needs and expectations; and managing the flow of materials into, through, and out of the system, all at an optimal life cycle cost. The elements of logistics are manpower and personal resources, maintenance, supply support, support and test equipment, transportation, training, technical documentation, computer resources, and facilities. In addition, design interfaces of reliability and maintainability are key logistics elements. Figure 11-3 shows the principal elements of logistics.

Manpower and personnel resources   People are the essential element of any system or process. As a logistics element, the organization must ensure that the right people with the right skills are available at the right time to do the right thing. Another important aspect of the people element of logistics is the man-machine interface.

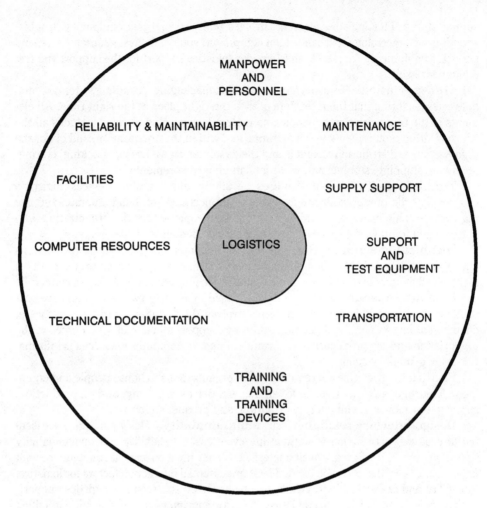

Fig. 11-3. Elements of logistics.

Maintenance   The maintenance of all equipment is critical to customer supportability. This includes the maintenance of all equipment within the organization and maintenance support of the product. Logistics must provide the right people, equipment, material, and tools at the right time in the right quantity to repair, modify, or prevent the breakdown of equipment. This could include field or customer service support.

Supply support   Supply support is needed for incoming supplies, kitting, work in-process, finished goods, and customer support. Having the right item at the right time in the right quantity is the focus of supply support. For supply support, logistics must determine requirements, receive, catalog, inspect, store, inventory, order, dispose, issue, and distribute all supplies.

Support and test equipment   Support and test equipment includes added equipment to facilitate the maintenance and repair of internal equipment and product supportability. This logistics element involves tools, special test equipment, trouble-shooting sets, metrology and calibration equipment, stands, dollies, generator sets, and servicing equipment. Frequently this includes logistics support for the support and test equipment itself.

Transportation Transportation includes packaging, handling, storage, and deliveries, ensuring that the right item gets to the right place at the right time. All elements of the transportation of people and materials are included. This includes all the transportation requirements to the organization, within the organization, and out of the organization to distribution channels and the customer, as well as any packing, crating, receiving, shipping, storage, and material handling requirements.

Training and training devices Training and training devices logistic's ensures that the proper skills are available to support, design, build, operate, and use the system. This includes providing training for people within the organization who perform and improve the process, customer service people, and customers.

Technical documentation Technical documentation provides instructions and procedures needed to maintain, operate, and use equipment or products. This includes all documentation of a technical nature for internal and external customers.

Computer resources Computers are used by many organizations and are part of many products. This logistics element involves the facilities, hardware, software, documentation, training, and people required to support all computer resources in the organization and the product. An important element of computer resources is information management systems.

Facilities Facilities are required for all organizations to house people and equipment. This logistics element includes all the facilities for receiving, design, production, support, warehousing, shipping, distribution, and product support.

Design interface reliability and maintainability Design interface is essential to customer satisfaction at optimal life cycle costs. Reliability and maintainability (R&M) are two of the primary design interfaces. They must ensure that an item does not fail and, if it does, that it can be fixed. These are essential interaction factors for logistics. Reliability and maintainability have a direct impact on the required logistics support. Reliability is the probability that an item will perform its intended function without failing for a specified period of time under specified conditions. Maintainability concerns the repair of an item once it fails. Reliability and maintainability are two of the primary drives of availability of the product for intended use when it is needed. R&M, along with logistics consideration, are major contributors to customer satisfaction.

Key points

- An economic war requires the never-ending achievement of victories.
- Victory is the vision and mission of the organization.
- Total customer satisfaction is the objective.
- Flexible, rapid response is the strategy.
- Highest-quality product and service at optimal life cycle cost are the tactics.
- The continuous improvement of systems and processes, involvement of people, and minimization of loss are the major operations.
- Numerous weapon systems are available to achieve victories.

- Today, many weapon systems use the latest technology to advantage. Remember to keep a proper balance of people and technology.
- Numerous other weapon systems are available to strive for victories. Some of the more common systems include just-in-time (JIT); total production maintenance (TPM); mistake proofing; total customer service (TCS); manufacturing resource planning (MRPII); computer-aided design, computer-aided engineering, and computer-aided manufacturing (CAD/CAE/CAM); computer integrated manufacturing (CIM); computer systems; information systems (IS); and total integrated logistics (TIL).
- Total integrated logistics, the secret weapon, can make a major difference in economic war; it can have a substantial impact on victory.
- Logistics is a process involved in all parts of the process: the input, the process itself, and the output to the customer.
- Logistics is an essential element of both the military and business environment.
- Total integrated logistics (TIL) is the integration of all the logistics elements involved in the inputs to the organization, the processes within the organization, and the outputs of the organization to ensure customer supportability at an optimal life cycle cost.
- Total integrated logistics focuses on supplier, process, and customer logistics for total customer satisfaction.
- The elements of logistics are manpower and personnel (people) resources, maintenance, supply support, support and test equipment, transportation, training, technical documentation, computer resources, and facilities. In addition, the design interfaces of reliability and maintainability are key logistics elements.

12

TQM in the Department of Defense

In the operations of war, where there are in a field of a thousand swift chariots, ten thousand heavy chariots, and a hundred thousand mail-clad soldiers, with provisions enough to carry them a thousand li, the expenditure at home and at the front, including entertainment of guests, small items such as glue and paint, and sums spent on chariots and armor, will reach the total of a thousand ounces of silver per day. Such is the cost of raising an army of a hundred thousand men.

Sun Tzu
The Art of War

This chapter describes Total Quality Management implementation within the U.S. Department of Defense (DoD). It provides an example of TQM tailored for a specific organization in the public sector and could be used as a guide for other public sector applications of Total Quality Management. Although the information in this chapter follows the outline of previous chapters of this book for a consistent approach, it is presented, as much as is possible, as it appears in actual DoD publications in order to ensure the integrity of the concepts. Overall, the chapter describes what TQM is to DoD, why TQM exists in DoD, what DoD is doing to achieve victory, how the DoD is achieving victory, a sample DoD improvement methodology with the TQM tools and techniques used in the DoD, and the specific application of the TQM philosophy and guiding principles in a system improvement document. In addition, some weapon systems particular to the Department of Defense are described to illustrate the institutionalization of Total Quality Management in many critical areas of the DoD.

What Total Quality Management is to DoD

The Department of Defense formally initiated TQM efforts in 1988 as a way of making improvements within the DoD and defense industry to ensure an adequate national defense, within budget. With the issue of a memorandum from the Secretary of Defense in 1988, TQM became a top priority in the Department of Defense. In that same year, the Under Secretary of Defense for Acquisition directed the implementation of TQM in the acquisition process.

Although TQM formally started in the DoD in 1988, several logistics agencies began using the TQM philosophy and guiding principles in the early 1980s to improve the quality and productivity of logistics activities. This is typical of initial TQM implementation. In many organizations, TQM is adopted as a grassroots movement in one part of the organization that feels a sense of urgency, the threat of competition, the necessity to provide the customer better value, or quite simply the need to survive. Sometime later, the organization realizes the need for Total Quality Management, throughout the entire organization. The organization then determines the most critical areas in which to implement TQM, and adopts it in these critical areas first. Once success is evident, TQM spreads throughout the entire organization.

DoD TQM definition

One DoD definition of Total Quality Management is presented in chapter 1 of this book. As stated in chapter 1, there are many other definitions of TQM. In fact, there are several within the DoD. Another definition of TQM from the DoD fact sheet on TQM states, "Total Quality Management is a customer oriented management approach. This approach stresses effective use of human resources and the application of the quantitative methods to continuously improve products and services by focusing on processes." This definition includes all of the essential elements of TQM, that is, continuous process improvement, people orientation, quantitative methods, and customer focus.

DoD TQM philosophy

The DoD philosophy of Total Quality Management is contained in the DoD posture on quality, as stated in a March 30, 1988 memorandum from the Secretary of Defense. The DoD posture on quality emphasizes the concepts required for continuously improving America's defense organizations. Figure 12-1 shows the DoD posture on quality.

DoD TQM principles

The basic Total Quality Management principles for the Department of Defense are outlined in a DoD pamphlet published by Secretary of Defense Frank Carlucci. These principles define the basic fundamental concepts, give rules for management action, and provide a framework for measurement. This pamphlet states that the DoD TQM principles are:

- *Continuous process improvement*

  The primary TQM objective is unending improvement of every aspect of DoD's work. That objective is implemented through a structured, disciplined approach that improves all processes. With TQM, emphasis is placed on preventing defects through process improvement rather than discovering them through product inspection.

- *Process knowledge*

  Process knowledge is essential for positive change. Since positive change is primarily created through process improvement ideas generated by those who work within the process, they must thoroughly understand their processes.

- *User focus*

  User response and mission performance are the absolute tests of DoD's effectiveness. Although Service members are the ultimate users of DoD products, each and every DoD process also has dependent, intermediate users. A thorough understanding of the needs of all users, intermediate or ultimate, not only provides the means for assessing performance, it also helps DoD focus its future direction and establish its future goals.

- *Commitment*

  Top leadership ensures DoD's strong, pervasive commitment to continuous improvement. Cost reduction, schedule compliance, customer satisfaction, and pride in workmanship all flow from an overt dedication to continuous improvement. Acting on recommendations to make positive changes demonstrates commitment to improvement.

- *Top-down implementation*

  TQM will first be implemented by top DoD leadership and flow down as a waterfall. This cascading deployment ensures that DoD leaders understand, demonstrate, and can teach TQM principles and practices before expecting them from, and evaluating them in, their subordinates.

- *Constancy of purpose*

  DoD leadership produces, communicates, and maintains a common purpose, with all DoD personnel working toward that purpose. Consistent goals and objectives provide focus and are realized through practicing continuous improvement and recognizing and rewarding behavior aimed at achieving the purpose.

- *Total involvement*

  Because all products and services are produced through processes, process improvement applies to every individual in DoD.

- *Teamwork*

  Teamwork is essential for continuous improvement. Teamwork and team structure align goals, objectives, and thought. Team activities build communication and cooperation, stimulate creative thought, and provide an infrastructure supporting TQM practices.

• *Investment in people*

DoD's largest and most valuable investment is in its people. They provide the knowledge and experience on which DoD relies. They are the most essential component in continuous process improvement. Training, team-building, and work-life enhancements are important elements in creating an environment in which our people can grow, gain experience and capability, and contribute to the national defense on an ever-increasing scale.

THE SECRETARY OF DEFENSE
WASHINGTON, THE DISTRICT OF COLUMBIA

DoD POSTURE ON QUALITY

• *Quality is absolutely vital to our defense, and requires a commitment to continuous improvement by all DoD personnel.*

• *A quality and productivity oriented Defense Industry with its underlying industrial base is the key to our ability to maintain a superior level of readiness.*

• *Sustained DoD wide emphasis and concern with respect to high quality and productivity must be an integral part of our daily activities.*

• *Quality improvement is a key to productivity improvement and must be pursued with the necessary resources to produce tangible benefits.*

• *Technology, being one of our greatest assets, must be widely used to improve continuously the quality of Defense systems, equipments and services.*

• *Emphasis must change from relying on inspection, to designing and building quality into the process and product.*

• *Quality must be a key element of competition.*

• *Acquisition strategies must include requirements for continuous improvement of quality and reduced ownership costs.*

• *Managers and personnel at all levels must take responsibility for the quality of their efforts.*

• *Competent, dedicated employees make the greatest contributions to quality and productivity. They must be recognized and rewarded accordingly.*

• *Quality concepts must be ingrained throughout every organization with the proper training at each level, starting with top management.*

• *Principles of quality improvement must involve all personnel and products, including the generation of products in paper and data form.*

Frank Carlucci

Fig. 12-1. DoD posture on quality.

Why Total Quality Management exists in the DoD

The Department of Defense is no exception to the impact of the tremendous changes in today's world. During these critical times, the DoD requires a greater level of performance within current budgets. The DoD can no longer afford any waste. As the Under Secretary of Defense for Acquisition states in memorandum of August 19, 1988, "The Department of Defense is facing one of the most challenging periods in its history. We must maintain the important gains in readiness already made and at the same time continue steady improvement in the face of greater austerity, increasing technological complexity, and a growing diversity of threats." He further states, "We believe that Total Quality Management can provide the leverage to meet these unparalleled challenges."

TQM works in the DoD environment. The DoD has been using the TQM concepts to improve logistics activities for a number of years. Many examples of success in the DoD have been reported. The Navy F-14 fighter overhaul program reduced average overhaul costs from $1.6 to $1.2 million per aircraft. The Naval Aviation Depot in Cherry Point, North Carolina, reported major quality, productivity, and cost improvement results. Navy Air Systems Command was the first to receive the prestigious President's Award for Quality and Productivity Improvement in 1989. Within the government, this award equals the Commerce Department's Malcolm Baldrige National Quality Award for U.S. companies. The Navy is not alone. The Air Force Systems Command reports successes with TQM in the acquisition process. Some examples include major reductions in change order cycle time, a more timely and efficient personnel management system, and improved relationships with DoD contractor suppliers. The Army, especially the Army Materiel Command, has already made many improvements that contribute directly to increased customer satisfaction.

What DoD is doing to achieve victory

The DoD is doing what it takes to achieve victory: creating a TQM system that focuses on the customer.

Focusing on the customer

All DoD efforts are aimed at "the satisfied, quality-equipped, quality-supported soldier, sailor, airman and Marine." This is covered more fully later in the chapter.

Creating the TQM Environment

The DoD has started the Total Quality Management march toward victory. The DoD has a vision, as well as the leadership to make the vision a reality. Leadership has started the process of involving everyone and everything in the improvement process. A focus on continuous improvement has been fostered. Training and education plans and actions have been initiated. Ownership of processes has been advocated. Reward and recognition are being emphasized. Years of commitment and support are already established.

Vision   The DoD vision is for "the most effective fighting force in the world, capable of handling all external challenges, while simultaneously meeting the economic pressures of affordability." This vision provides the purpose for the entire Department of Defense. Victory to the DoD in TQM means providing the best possible national defense within budget. This vision is a challenge that requires many changes within the DoD and the defense industry. Everyone in both the DoD and defense industry must accept the challenge to make this vision a reality.

Leadership The TQM concepts are being implemented by top leadership and are flowing to all levels of the organization. Leadership is responsible for creating and maintaining the TQM environment. The DoD leadership is committed to setting the example for others to follow.

Involvement The DoD has involved the DoD and the defense industry in TQM implementation.

TQM applies to all administrative, engineering, logistics, production, operational, and support functions. Leadership and all personnel participate in TQM activities, combined with new technology and procedures.

Because teamwork is an essential element of the DoD approach, the constant involvement of both functional and multifunctional teams is fostered.

The DoD approach also stresses the involvement of suppliers and customers in all activities.

Continuous improvement The DoD is pursuing continuous improvement in all activities. Leadership is committed to its support. The focus is on the never-ending improvement of every DoD process through a structured, disciplined approach; the emphasis is on defining the process, measuring performance, selecting opportunities for improvement (OFI), implementing OFIs, monitoring the process, and continually looking for further opportunities for improvement.

Training and education Training and education are cornerstones of the DoD TQM effort. Training and education programs include teaching skills for creating and maintaining the TQM environment; continuous improvement systems; teamwork; interpersonal skills; tools and techniques; planning and goal setting; organizational communication; and resource optimization principles, practices, and tools and techniques.

Ownership The DoD stresses everyone's responsibility for quality. Within the DoD, quality improvement is part of everyone's duties. All personnel are expected to work toward increasing customer satisfaction, improving performance, reducing cycle time, and decreasing costs.

Reward and recognition Reward and recognition for individual and team contributions are emphasized within the Department of Defense. In addition, the reward and recognition effort stresses adherence to the continuous improvement process.

For the defense industry, the reward is survival. Quality is a key element of competition. Contractors who provide "best value to the government by consistently demonstrating, through performance on production contracts, an ability to deliver on time while consistently improving quality and reducing cost should be rewarded for their accomplishment." This policy was stated in a May 1989 Deputy Secretary for Defense memorandum.

The DoD realizes that the success of TQM depends on a reward and recognition system reinforcing positive TQM actions. Its strategy is aimed at providing the proper incentives for TQM. Of course, the greatest reward is America's continuing freedom and security.

Years of commitment and support   The DoD leadership is committed to providing required resources and support to ensure that the vision becomes a reality. Presidential and congressional support will also be important in the future.

How DoD is achieving victory

As stated in chapter 4, a plan, a support system, and training are necessary to achieve victory. The DoD has initiated all of these elements in their implementation.

TQM master plan

The DoD *Total Quality Master Plan*, published in August 1988, outlines the DoD's TQM implementation strategy. The overall objective of the DoD plan is the continuous improvement of products and services in all DoD activities. This includes weapons, systems, functions, processes, tasks, and actions. It involves acquisition, logistics, design, maintenance, supply, personnel, training, administration, and all other functions. The master plan stresses the importance of people in the continuous improvement process. It involves everyone.

The master plan emphasizes the successful implementation of TQM and requires a nurturing, encouraging environment; a disciplined organizational methodology; and a formal, structured process improvement methodology.

The DoD TQM master plan advocates a methodology that starts with broad organizational goals and has subordinate goals and objectives that support the larger organizational goals. The goals are defined as long term, midrange, and short term. Long-term goals translate intangible improvement goals into broad areas for quantifiable action. Midrange goals support the overall premise by focusing the effort where major improvements are required. Short-term goals are specific targets or tasks.

The goals and objectives are converted into actions through the use of a continuous improvement cycle. Within the continuous improvement cycle, specific tools and techniques assist in defining the process, generating and selecting improvements, and measuring and analyzing performance.

Each individual organization in the DoD develops its own TQM implementation plan based on the framework of the DoD TQM master plan. This ensures a consistent, organization-wide approach to TQM implementation.

DoD master plan goals

DoD long-term, midrange, and short-term goals are as follows:

Long-term goals (7 years)

- Establish TQM as a way of life.
- Involve all DoD personnel directly continuous process improvement.
- Achieve widespread defense industry implementation of continuous process improvement.
- Obtain congressional understanding of and support for TQM.

Midrange goals (3 years)

- Establish and implement policy deployment mechanisms.
- Harmonize DoD directives/regulations/instructions and TQM.
- Eliminate barriers to TQM implementation.
- Implementation commitment by major defense contractors, with "critical mass" achieved in at least the top 25 contractors.
- DoD Acquisition personnel use TQM principles and practices in dealing with industry.
- Develop, produce, acquire, and promulgate a standard set of TQM training materials.
- Establish a mature, functioning staff of facilitators.
- Understand and coordinate with the TQM efforts of other sectors of the Federal Government.
- Develop and cultivate key congressional TQM champions.

Short-term Goals (1 year)

- Establish Executive Steering Committee and subordinate teams, and begin training and continuous process improvement activities.
- Identify initial cadre of TQM facilitators and begin facilitating team activities and training staff facilitators.
- Implement the TQM training strategy and begin collecting and developing training materials.
- Establish a research and development (R&D) program in support of TQM.
- Develop and implement a recognition and reward system based on TQM goals and behaviors.
- Begin ensuring consistency among TQM and major documentation and guidance.
- Begin enlisting defense industry commitment.

Support system

The DoD has instituted a support system: the Executive Steering Committee, which determines the broad organizational goals. At each subordinate level, the existing organization works within existing work groups to pursue subordinate goals and objectives. The top-level DoD support structure is shown in FIG. 12-2. In the figure, the Defense Council on Integrity and Management Improvement (DCIMI) forms the Executive Steering Committee. The Executive Steering Committee will form teams, and these teams will start other teams throughout the DoD. This support structure will be promulgated throughout the DoD to ensure an emphasis on the critical aspects of TQM.

Facilitators   The DoD is actively working to ensure that TQM facilitators are in place and working at all levels to implement TQM. The facilitators' duties include assisting in implementation, training, and monitoring progress.

Trainers   Trainers are key elements of the DoD implementation approach. The DoD is pursuing a complete training package for TQM. This includes a variety of training methods from individual study to formal training.

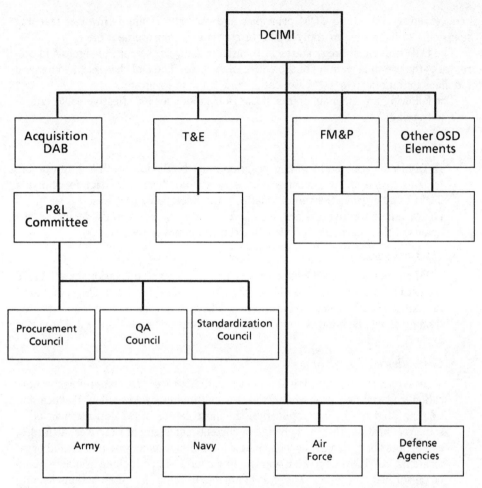

Fig. 12-2. DoD TQM infrastructure from the DoD TQM master plan. DCIMI, Defense Council on Integrity and Management Improvement; DAB, Defense Acquisition Board; T&E, Training and Education; FM&P, Funding, Manpower and Personnel; OSD, Office of Secretary of Defense; P&L, Production and Logistics; QA, Quality Assurance.

Training and education Training is an essential element of creating and maintaining the Total Quality Management environment within the DoD. The DoD TQM strategy is outlined in *An Education and Training Strategy for Total Quality Management in the Department of Defense*, published in July 1989. The ultimate goal of the training effort is to institutionalize TQM. The DoD training strategy seeks to optimize the TQM training resources within the DoD by using to advantage the capabilities developed within the logistics areas and employing existing DoD education and training institutions, supplemented by external resources.

The DoD training and education strategy addresses both training and education needs for TQM. TQM requires both education and training to be successful. Education is concerned with teaching TQM principles and concepts. Training involves teaching the specific skills needed to apply TQM for continuous improvement efforts.

The DoD training strategy starts with initial training for senior managers and progresses to the eventual training of the entire work force. The DoD has outlined general guidelines for an effective TQM Education and Training Program.

The following are the main points of the DoD guidelines for effective TQM education and training:

- *Flexibility*

  A TQM education and training program must be flexible so that it can be tailored to the specific organization. Since there is no "best" approach for applying TQM to all organizations and situations, the Secretary of Defense issues broad policy, but the individual Services and Defense agencies must decide on the details of their particular education and training programs.

- *Top-down commitment*

  TQM starts from a top-down commitment. Training and education must include the active involvement of top leadership. In addition, top leadership must have the skills to set the example for others to follow. A key element of top-leadership training should be information about how to institutionalize TQM within the various organizations.

- *Continuing cycle of education*

  TQM education and training are a never-ending process. A comprehensive education and training program includes a continuing cycle of TQM education, training, and on-the-job application. In most cases, TQM education involves some reeducation, that is, a change in current management practices, attitudes, and beliefs about quality, as well as new ideas about managing people and organizations. All TQM education and training courses must include assignments to be performed on the job. Those assignments become the initial actions leading to implementation. Follow-up on the education process is necessary for feedback, for obtaining new information, and for evaluation.

- *Broad focus*

  An effective TQM education and training program includes the entire work force, the suppliers, and the customers. It should cover such areas as quality awareness and TQM philosophy; quantitative methods for analyzing processes; group development skills, such as team building and effective communication, especially listening; and knowledge about how to change organizational culture and overcome obstacles in order to implement TQM. All TQM education and training should be delivered "just-in-time" as it is needed in an organization.

A TQM education and training program should include suppliers and customers, cost considerations, and delivery methods: Suppliers and customers should be brought into formal relationship with the organization; Costs of TQM training must be geared to provide the desired results; Delivery of education and training should consider the existing infrastructure before new mechanisms are established.

The DoD list of potential topics, methods, and tools applicable to TQM education and training is shown below.

TQM topics, methods, and tools

I.   Awareness

    A. Overview of the quality problem (worldwide, U.S. government)

       1. The threat and challenge of foreign competition

       2. Quality of American products and services

    B. History of management, quality focus and control, and quality management

       1. Post-WWII management philosophies

       2. Management-worker values, relations and attitudes

    C. Definition of quality (quality in government/DoD)

    D. Achieving quality

       1. Detection versus prevention approach

       2. Definition and examples of process

    E. Definition and explanation of Total Quality Management (TQM)

II. TQM philosophy and key concepts

    A. Production viewed as a system

    B. Cost of quality

       1. Cost of detection

       2. Visible versus hidden costs

       3. Cost of quality categories (internal and external failure, appraisal, exceeding requirements, lost opportunities, "unknown-unknowable," prevention)

    C. The chain reaction of quality and productivity

    D. The paradigm shift (from machine age thinking to systems age thinking)

    E. Management of outcomes versus management of processes

    F. Continuous improvement

    G. Variation: common and special causes

    H. Taguchi loss function

    I. Customer orientation (customer-supplier relations)

    J. Cross-functional management teams

    K. Four prongs of quality

III. Basic methods and tools

    A. Scientific method: Plan-Do-Check-Act cycle and Process Improvement Model

    B. Process capability analysis (process control and customer requirements)

    C. Process analysis, control, and improvement process

    D. Basic descriptive and graphics methods

       1. Basic graphics tools

          a. Flowchart

          b. Cause-and-effect (fishbone) diagram

          c. Pareto chart

          d. Histogram

          e. Scatter diagram

          f. Run chart

          g. Control chart

       2. Management and planning tools

          a. Affinity chart

          b. Interrelationship diagram

          c. Tree diagram

          d. Matrix chart

          e. Matrix-data analysis

          f. Process decision program chart

          g. Arrow diagram

          h. Check list

          i. Stratification matrix

    F. Fundamentals of measurement

       1. Data collection and measurement

       2. Qualitative and quantitative data

       3. Factors that affect measurement

       4. Outcome vs. process measures

    G. Fundamentals of experimental design (baselining, pre-post comparisons)

IV. Management responsibility and leadership

    A. Vision and philosophy

    B. Management practices to support TQM

    C. TQM strategic planning and decision making

    D. Organizational TQM structures

    E. Policy deployment

    F. Customer satisfaction

    G. Customer-supplier interface

    H. Implementation process/guidelines

    I. Creating the organizational culture

       1. Management of participation

       2. TQM leadership

          a. Leading by example

          b. Role of guide, mentor, teacher

        c. Personal responsibility for quality
        d. Team building and group facilitation

V.   Group dynamic skills

   A. Group dynamics and team building (overcoming resistance)

   B. Effective communication

   C. Group problem solving (brainstorming, nominal group technique)

   D. Win-win strategy: agreement, alignment

   E. Negotiation and conflict resolution

   F. Purpose and focus

VI. TQM implementation

   A. Organizational TQM structures

   B. Developing the implementation plan (short- and long-term)

   C. TQM education and training strategy

   D. Creating the organizational culture

       1. Implementing the 14 points (Deming)
       2. Overcoming obstacles
       3. Combating the deadly and dreadful diseases
       4. Cooperation and teamwork: cross-functional teams

   E. Quality improvement process (PDCA)

VII. Advanced methods

   A. Advanced scientific methodology

   B. Quality function deployment (QFD)

   C. Quality policy deployment (QPD)

   D. Off-line experimental methods and processes

       1. System design, concurrent engineering
       2. Parameter and tolerance design (design of experiments, Taguchi approaches)
       3. Inventory control/product engineering

   E. On-Line experimental methods and processes

       1. Measurement engineering
       2. Process control and improvement

   F. Socio-technical design of work

       1. Integration of human and technical systems
       2. Methodology for work system design

Continuous improvement system

Many continuous improvement systems are in use, even within the DoD. Chapter 4 in this book provides one example of a continuous improvement system. Several others are described in the *Draft Department of Defense Total Quality Management Guide.*

Each organization must select or create one continuous improvement system to be used throughout the organization to ensure consistency. A typical continuous improvement system from the *Draft Department of Defense Total Quality Management Guide* is shown in FIG. 12-3. This DSMC/ATI model has seven steps:

Step 1 Establish the TQM management and cultural environment.

This step requires top-management action. Top management must have a vision, maintain a long-term commitment, involve all people in improvement efforts, use a disciplined approach involving appropriate tools and techniques, establish a support system, and provide training and education.

Step 2 Define the mission of each component of the organization.

Step 3 Set performance improvement opportunities, goals, and priorities.

Step 4 Establish improvement projects and action plans.

Step 5 Implement projects using improvement methodologies.

Step 6 Evaluate.

In this step, improve performance by reducing cycle time, lowering costs, and innovating.

Step 7 Review and recycle.

Customer satisfaction

The Department of Defense Total Quality Management process focuses on "the satisfied, quality-equipped, quality-supported soldier, sailor, airman and Marine." This is the ultimate customer. The DoD emphasizes providing customers with the products and services that consistently meet their needs and expectations. The customer is both the internal customer and the external customer. The DoD advocates not only meeting customer needs but also anticipating them.

The DoD also stresses satisfying true customer requirements. This necessitates a complete knowledge of the customer's needs and expectations. Meeting the customer's needs and expectations is the responsibility of the supplier, the process owner, and the customer.

Improvement methodology

Almost as many improvement methodologies for continuous improvement are available as there are organizations using TQM. Each organization selects or establishes an improvement methodology appropriate to its specific requirements. One improvement methodology is shown in chapter 5 of this book. Most improvement methodologies are

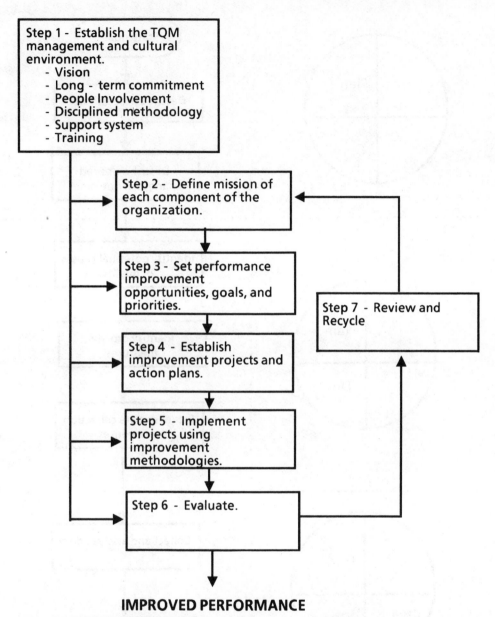

Step 1 - Establish the TQM management and cultural environment.
  - Vision
  - Long - term commitment
  - People Involvement
  - Disciplined methodology
  - Support system
  - Training

Step 2 - Define mission of each component of the organization.

Step 3 - Set performance improvement opportunities, goals, and priorities.

Step 4 - Establish improvement projects and action plans.

Step 5 - Implement projects using improvement methodologies.

Step 6 - Evaluate.

Step 7 - Review and Recycle

IMPROVED PERFORMANCE

Fig. 12-3. Typical TQM continuous improvement model from Draft Department of Defense Total Quality Management Guide.

based on problem-solving methodologies. Other popular improvement methodologies are based on the Deming or plan, do, check, act (PDCA) cycle. An example of an improvement methodology based on the PDCA cycle that is used within the Department of Defense is shown in FIG. 12-4. This Navy Personnel Research and Development Center (NPRDC) model was developed to improve the quality and productivity of the

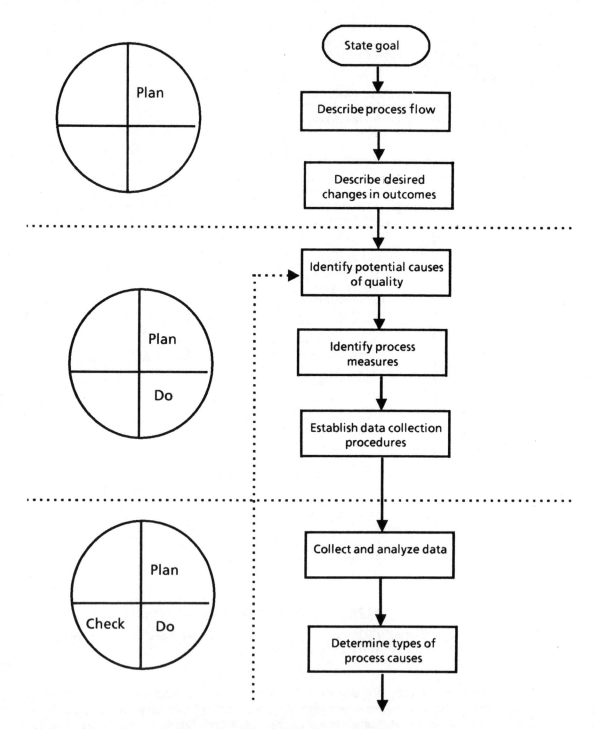

Fig. 12-4. TQM process improvement model from Navy Personnel Research and Development Center.

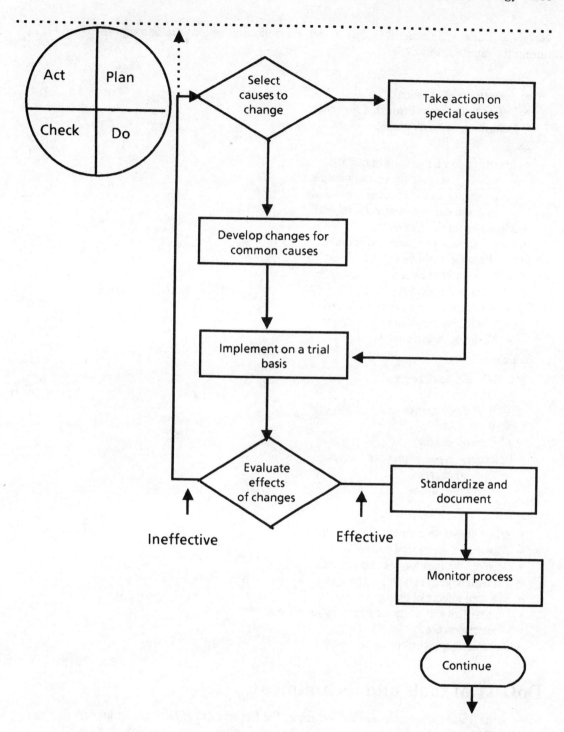

Navy's logistics organizations. In this model, the following actions are accomplished during the improvement cycle:

Plan

- State the goal (mission).
- Define the process through a flowchart.
- Determine desired outcomes.

Do

- Identify potential causes of quality.
  - ~ develop baseline for process outputs.
  - ~ construct an as-is process flowchart.
  - ~ perform cause-and-effect analysis.
- Identify process measures.
- Establish data collection procedures.
  - ~ What data will be collected?
  - ~ How will the data be collected?
  - ~ Who will collect the data?
  - ~ Where will the data be collected?
  - ~ When will the data be collected?
  - ~ Perform Pareto analysis.

Check

- Collect and analyze data.
  - ~ Histograms
  - ~ Scatter diagrams
  - ~ Run charts
  - ~ Control charts
- Determine types of process causes.
  - ~ Special causes
  - ~ Common causes

Act

- Select causes to change.
- Take action on special causes.
- Develop changes for common causes.
- Implement common cause changes on a trial basis.
- Evaluate effects of changes.
- Standardize and document process improvements.
- Monitor process.
- Continue improvement cycle.

DoD TQM tools and techniques

Some of the TQM tools recommended for use by the Department of Defense for implementing TQM are shown in FIG. 12-5. The figure indicates where the tools can be

TOOLS & TECHNIQUES	PROBLEM-SOLVING ACTIVITIES					
	BOUNDS & PRIORITIZE PROBLEMS	Compile Information	Analysis	General Alternatives	Evaluate	Plan & Implement
Benchmarking	X	X	X		X	
Cause & Effect Diagram	X		X			
Nominal Group Technique	X	X		X	X	X
Quality Function Deployment	X		X		X	
Pareto Charts	X	X	X			
Statistical Process Control		X	X			
Histograms		X	X			
Check Sheets		X	X			
Input/Output Analysis			X			
Scatter Diagrams			X			
Concurrent Engineering			X	X		
Design of Experiments			X	X	X	
Cost of Quality			X		X	
Control Charts			X		X	
Work Flow Analysis			X			X
Team Building						X
Time Management	X					X
Shewart/Deming Cycle	X	X	X	X	X	X

Fig. 12-5. Common TQM tools and techniques from Draft Department of Defense Total Quality Management Guide.

applied in problem-solving activities. Most of these tools and techniques are described in this book in chapters 6 through 10.

DoD system improvement

The defense acquisition process is one of the primary areas of emphasis for TQM implementation, and system improvement is a large concern in defense acquisition.

System improvement example: the TQM template for DoD 4245.7-M

One example of the implementation of the IQM approach in the DoD is the incorporation of TQM principles in DoD 4245.7-M, *Transition from Development to Production*. This document is a primary tool for the development and production of systems. The TQM template in DoD 4245.7-M is shown below. Figure 12-6 is a TQM flowchart.

Introduction for TQM Critical Path Template

Since publication of this Manual in September 1985, a major New DoD initiative has been instituted called TQM. Change 1 to this Manual provides additional guidance to implement the philosophy and managerial approach involved with TQM and consists of a new template inserted in chapter 1. The new template aggregates TQM provisions now contained in the Manual by highlighting key DESIGN, TEST, and PRODUCTION template activity and identifying certain advances in TQM methods and techniques that have come to prominence. Pending a more extensive revision to this Manual, guidance in the TQM template shall take precedence in the event of conflict with other templates.

TQM is the disciplined process of continuous improvement in performance at every level and in all areas of responsibility within the Department of Defense. Improved performance is directed toward goals assigned to cost, schedule, mission need, and operational suitability. Increasing "user" satisfaction is the paramount objective. Whereas this Manual concentrates on the industrial process concerned with the acquisition of material, TQM principles are applicable equally to supporting functions and military operations.

TQM was approved for application DoD-wide by the Secretary of Defense on March 30, 1988, assigning it "top priority." The DoD posture statement on quality is reproduced on page 1-17. On August 30, 1988, the Under Secretary of Defense for Acquisition issued direction to implement TQM in the acquisition process and called for a climate in both Government and industry that would foster TQM implementation.

The TQM template is portrayed at the top of the template network in FIG. 1-2, directly supporting the product. By "product" is meant systems, equipments, hardware, or software, and supporting services. TQM affects everything the Department of Defense produces, procures, or performs. It is appropriate to all templates and nonacquisition activities. TQM requires professional discipline and commitment from both the Department of Defense and industry.

Area of risk

TQM is an organized process of continuous improvement by private defense contractors and DoD activities aimed at developing, producing, and deploying superior materiel. The primary threat to reaching and sustaining this superiority is failure to manage with a purpose of constantly increasing intrinsic quality, economic value, and military worth of defense systems and equipments. The Armed Forces and defense industrial

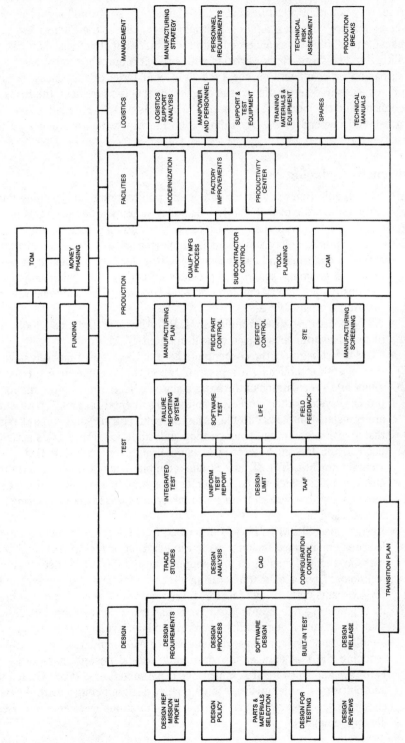

Fig. 12-6. DoD Total Quality Management flowchart.

entities may not attain a lasting competitive military posture and long-term competitive business stature without a total commitment to quality at the highest levels. TQM is applicable to all functions concerned with the acquisition of defense material, supplies, facilities, and services. Being satisfied with sub-optimum, short-term goals and objectives has adverse impacts on cost, schedule, and force effectiveness. A short-term approach leads to deterioration in the efficacy of specific products, the firms that produce them, and the industrial base overall. Major risk also is entailed with the inability to grasp and respond to the overriding importance attached to quality by the "customer" or user activities.

Outline for reducing risk

- The organization has a "corporate level" policy statement attaching highest priority to the principles of TQM. This policy statement defines TQM in terms relevant to the individual enterprise or activity and its products or outputs.
- The corporate policy statement is supported by a TQM implementation plan that sets enduring and long-range objectives, list, criteria for applying TQM to new and on-going programs, provides direction and guidance, and assigns responsibilities. Every employee at each level plays a functional role in implementing the plan.
- All personnel are given training in TQM principles, practices, tools, and techniques. Importance is placed on self-initiated TQM effort.
- TQM effort begun in the conceptual phase of the acquisition cycle is vitally concerned with establishing a rapport between the producer and the user or customer and a recognition of the latter's stated performance requirements, mission profiles, system characteristics, and environmental factors. Those statements are translated into measurable design, manufacturing, and support parameters that are verified during demonstration and validation. Early TQM activity is outlined in the Design Reference Mission Profile template and Design Requirements template. The Trade Studies template is used to identify potential characteristics which would accelerate design maturity while making the design more compatible with and less sensitive to variations in manufacturing and operational conditions.
- Design phase TQM activity is described in the Design Process template. Key features enumerated include: design integration of life-cycle factors concerned with production, operation, and support; availability of needed manufacturing technology; proof of manufacturing process; formation of design and design review teams with various functional area representation; and use of producibility engineering and planning to arrive at and transition a producible design to the shop floor without degradation in quality and performance. The Design Analysis template and Design Reviews template provide guidance in identifying and reducing the risk entailed in controlling critical design characteristics. Both hardware and software are emphasized (reference the Software Design template and Software Test template). A high quality design includes features to enhance conducting necessary test and inspection functions (reference the Design for Testing template).

- An integrated test plan of contractor development, qualification, and production acceptance testing and a test and evaluation master plan (TEMP) covering Government-related testing are essential to TQM. The plans detail sufficient testing to prove conclusively the design, its operational suitability, and its potential for required growth and future utility. Test planning also makes efficient use of test articles, test facilities, and other resources. Failure reporting, field feedback, and problem disposition are vital mechanisms to obtaining a quality product.
- Manufacturing planning bears the same relationship to production success as test planning bears to a successful test program (reference the Manufacturing Plan template). The overall acquisition strategy includes a manufacturing strategy and a transition plan covering all production-related activities. Equal care and emphasis is placed on proof of manufacture as well as on proving the design itself. The Quality Manufacturing template highlights production planning, tooling, manufacturing methods, facilities, equipment, and personnel. Extreme importance is attached to subcontractor and vendor selection and qualification including flow down in the use of TQM principles. Special test equipment, computer-aided manufacturing, and other advanced equipments and statistical based methods are used to qualify and control the manufacturing process.

TQM is used throughout the product life-cycle

TQM oriented defense contractors and government activities concentrate on designing and building quality into their products at the outset. Successful activities are not content with the status quo or acceptable level of quality approach. Those activities respond to problems affecting product quality by changing the design and/or the process, not by increasing inspection levels. Reduction in variability of the detail design and the manufacturing process is a central concept of TQM and is beneficial to lower cost as well as higher quality. Defect prevention is viewed as key to defect control. Astute TQM activities are constantly on the alert to identify and exploit new and proven managerial, engineering, and manufacturing disciplines and associated techniques.

Area of risk, DoD 4245.7-M   This excerpt from DoD 4245.7-M stresses the following Total Quality Management principles:

- Continuous improvement
- Total commitment to quality
- Involvement of many functions
- Long-term improvement effort
- Customer focus

Outline for reducing risk, DoD 4245.7-M   This part of DoD 4245.7-M incorporates the following TQM principles. It:

- Includes a policy statement (vision/mission)
- Pursues a TQM environment
- Stresses a TQM implementation plan
- Fosters ownership

- Advocates training
- Includes quality as an element of design
- Encourages measurements
- Includes everything and everyone
- Nurtures supplier and customer relationships
- Encourages cooperation and teamwork

TQM is used throughout the product life cycle, from DoD 4245.7-M
This part of DoD 4245.7-M highlights the need for:

- Quality as an element of design
- Continuous improvement geared to reduction in variability
- Focus on prevention of defects
- Use of fundamental management techniques, existing improvement efforts, and technical tools under a disciplined approach allowing creativity and innovation

TQM weapon systems within the DoD

Many TQM weapon systems in addition to those described in chapter 11 are used specifically by the Department of Defense. Some examples of the more specific DoD TQM weapon systems include Computer-Aided Acquisition and Logistics Support (CALS), In-Plant Quality Evaluation Program (IQUE), Reliability and Maintainability 2000 (R&M 2000), and Value Engineering (VE). This is not an all-inclusive list. The DoD has many TQM weapon systems being used in all its agencies to improve continuously its processes, with the focus on customer satisfaction.

Computer-Aided Acquisition and Logistics Support

The Computer-Aided Acquisition and Logistics Support (CALS) program is a strategy to institute within DoD and industry an integrated "system of systems" in order to create, transmit, and use technical information in digital form to design, manufacture, and support weapon systems and equipment, and to apply communication and computer technology to the acquisition and support of major weapon systems and information systems. CALS can integrate automation between the DoD contractor and DoD. It is a Department of Defense program to acquire, manage, access, and distribute weapon systems information more efficiently. This includes all acquisition, design, manufacturing, and logistics information. CALS focuses on increasing reliability, maintainability, and availability through the integration of automation systems. In addition, CALS seeks to improve the productivity, quality, and timeliness of logistics support while reducing costs.

In-Plant Quality Evaluation

The In-Plant Quality Evaluation (IQUE) program changes the traditional methods by which in-plant government people evaluate contractor controls over product quality. A TQM approach is used instead. The IQUE approach focuses on measuring and continuously improving processes with the aim toward quality (customer satisfaction). It concentrates on the what versus the how. The government provides the what, and the contractor determines the how. IQUE implements a cooperative team concept between government and contractors.

Reliability and Maintainability 2000

The Reliability and Maintainability (R&M) 2000 approach is geared to increasing combat capability while reducing costs through R&M practices. It also stresses continuous improvements in R&M to increase combat availability and reduce logistics support requirements.

The R&M 2000 program builds on TQM principles. It stresses the need for management involvement (leadership), requirements (vision/mission, involvement of everyone and everything focused on customer satisfaction), preservation (continuous improvement of processes and years of commitment and support), design and growth (training and ownership), and motivation (reward and recognition).

Value Engineering

Value Engineering (VE) is an organized effort directed at analyzing the function of systems, equipment, facilities, services, and supplies for the purpose of achieving essential functions at the lowest life cycle cost consistent with performance, reliability, maintainability, interchangeability, product quality, and safety. This definition comes from DoD Directive 4245.8. This specific DoD weapon system for TQM again stresses the need to improve quality and productivity from DoD and DoD contractors while reducing cost.

Key points

- The Department of Defense is taking the necessary steps to implement Total Quality Management.
- The implementation of TQM within the DoD has been modified for the specific vision and organizational environment of the DoD.
- The DoD principles focus on:
    - ~ Continuous process improvement
    - ~ Process knowledge
    - ~ Focus on customer
    - ~ Commitment
    - ~ Top-down implementation
    - ~ Constancy of purpose
    - ~ Total involvement
    - ~ Teamwork
    - ~ Investment in people
- Total Quality Management is working in many areas of the DoD.
- The DoD has started its march toward victory by instituting all the required elements of victory, focusing on the customer.

- The DoD is creating a TQM environment with a plan, a support system, and training.
- A continuous improvement system has been established within the DoD.
- The Department of Defense recommended specific tools and techniques for improvement methodologies.
- The TQM approach has been incorporated in many DoD documents, including many focusing on systems improvements.

Appendices

Appendix A

Total Quality Management approaches

Among many approaches to TQM, those outlined below are some of the most popular. You will notice that they have more similarities than differences.

TQM approaches

The descriptions of the various TQM approaches give the expert's name, source reference, and approach highlights.

W. Edwards Deming approach

The following is an updated version of the original 14 points outlined in *Out of the Crisis*.* This version was provided in 1991 courtesy of W. Edwards Deming through the Massachusetts Institute of Technology, Center of Advanced Engineering Study.

1. Create and publish to all employees a statement of the aims and purposes of the company or other organization. The management must demonstrate constantly their commitment to this statement.
2. Learn the new philosophy, top management and everybody.
3. Understand the purpose of inspection, for improvement of processes and reduction of cost.
4. End the practice of awarding business on the basis of price tag alone.
5. Improve constantly and forever the system of production and service.
6. Institute training.
7. Teach and institute leadership.

---

*Adapted from *Out of the Crisis* by W. Edwards Deming by permission of MIT and W. Edwards Deming. Published by MIT, Center for Advanced Engineering Study, Cambridge, MA 02139. Copyright 1982 by W. Edwards Deming.

8. Drive out fear. Create trust. Create a climate for innovation.
9. Optimize toward the aims and purposes of the company the efforts of teams, groups, staff areas.
10. Eliminate exhortations for the work force.
11. a. Eliminate numerical quotas for production. Instead, learn and institute methods for improvement.
    b. Eliminate M.B.O. (Management by Objectives). Instead, learn the capabilities of processes, and how to improve them.
12. Remove barriers that rob people of pride of workmanship.
13. Encourage education and self-improvement for everyone.
14. Take action to accomplish the transformation.

Joseph Juran approach

The following is an outline of the Joseph Juran approach as provided by Juran Institute, Wilton, Connecticut.* Joseph Juran, author of many books on quality, bases his approach on three major processes. These processes titled, *The Juran Trilogy®* , consist of quality planning (design for quality), quality control, and quality improvement. The outline for the three processes is as follows:

Quality planning

Quality planning concerns the development of a product or a process. The quality planning approach follows:

- Identify the customers, both internal and external.
- Determine customer needs.
- Develop product features that can respond to customer needs.
- Establish quality goals that meet the needs of customers and suppliers alike and do so at a minimum combined cost.
- Develop a process that can produce the needed product features.
- Prove process capability—prove that the process can meet the quality goals under operating conditions.

Quality control

Quality control deals with keeping a process operation as planned. The basic quality control process is:

- Choose control subjects—what to control.
- Choose units of measurements.
- Establish measurements.
- Establish standards of performance.
- Measure actual performance.
- Interpret the difference (actual verus standard).
- Take action on the difference.

---

*Used with permission from the copyright holder, ©Juran Institute, Inc., Wilton, Connecticut, USA. *The Juran Trilogy* is a registered trademark of Juran Institute, Inc.

Quality improvement

Quality improvement focuses on attacking the levels of chronically poor quality and establishing new processes with improved quality. The quality improvement process is:

• Prove the need for improvement.
• Identify specific projects for improvement.
• Organize to guide the projects.
• Organize for diagnosis—for discovery of causes.
• Diagnose to find the causes.
• Provide remedies.
• Prove that the remedies are effective under operating conditions.
• Provide for contol to hold the gains.

Philip Crosby Zero Defect approach

The Philip Crosby approach for Zero Defects is outlined in *Quality Is Free*.* The major points are:

1. Management commitment
2. Quality improvement team
3. Quality measurement
4. Cost of quality evaluation
5. Quality awareness
6. Corrective action
7. Zero defects program
8. Supervisor training
9. Zero defects day
10. Goal setting
11. Error causes removal
12. Recognition
13. Quality councils
14. Do it over again

H. James Harrington Process Improvement approach

The H. James Harrington Process Improvement approach is described in his book *The Improvement Process*.* The approach is as follows:

1. Obtain top-management commitment.
2. Establish an improvement steering council.

---

*Adapted from *Quality Is Free* by Philip B. Crosby, McGraw-Hill, Inc., 1986. With permission of McGraw-Hill, Inc.

*Adapted from *The Improvement Process* by H. James Harrington, McGraw-Hill, Inc., 1987. With permission of McGraw-Hill, Inc.

3. Obtain total management participation.
4. Secure team participation.
5. Obtain individual involvement.
6. Establish system improvement teams.
7. Develop supplier involvement activities.
8. Establish a systems quality assurance activity.
9. Develop and implement short-range improvement plans and a long-range improvement strategy.
10. Establish a recognition program.

A. Richard Shores Total Quality Control approach

The A. Richard Shores Total Quality Control approach as outlined in his book *Survival of the Fittest*** follows:

1. Customer satisfaction
2. Management commitment
3. Total participation
4. Common process improvement framework
5. Statistical quality control tools

Department of Defense Disciplined Methodology approach

The Department of Defense approach is described in the *Draft Department of Defense Total Quality Management Guide*. The DoD approach is:

1. Establish the TQM management and cultural environment.
2. Define the mission of each component of the organization.
3. Set performance improvement opportunities, goals, and priorities.
4. Establish improvement projects and action plans.
5. Implement projects using improvement methodologies.
6. Evaluate.
7. Review and recycle.

Victory-C approach

The present author's victory-C approach is described in this book, *The Total Quality Management Field Manual*. It focuses all the elements of victory on customer satisfaction. The elements of victory are:

1. Determine the vision and provide leadership to make the vision reality.
2. Get everyone and everything involved to improve the process.
3. Establish a continuous improvement system.

**Adapted from *Survival of the Fittest*, A. Richard Shores, ASQC Quality, Press, 1986. With permission of ASQC Quality Press.

4. Provide training and education.
5. Establish ownership of all processes.
6. Institute a reward and recognition system.
7. Establish commitment and support.
8. Focus on total customer satisfaction for victory.

Appendix B

Malcolm Baldrige Award

This appendix describes the 1991 Malcolm Baldrige Award criteria. This information is given exactly as it appears in the 1991 Application Guidelines.* For further information, contact The Malcolm Baldrige National Quality Award office at the U.S. Department of Commerce, National Institute of Standards and Technology, Gaithersburg, Maryland 20899.

Description of the 1991 examination

The Award Examination is based upon criteria designed to be a quality excellence standard for organizations seeking the highest levels of overall quality performance and competitiveness. The Examination addresses all key requirements to achieve quality excellence as well as the important interrelationships among these key requirements. By focusing not only upon results but also upon the conditions and processes that lead to results, the Examination offers a framework that can be used by organizations to tailor their systems and processes toward ever-improving quality performance. Moreover, the mechanisms for tailoring are themselves included in the Examination.

Reliable evaluation relative to the Examination criteria requires considerable experience with quality systems. Nevertheless, the Examination may also be used for self-assessment and other purposes. Thousands of organizations—businesses, government, health care, and education—whether or not they are currently eligible or plan to apply for Awards, are using the Examination for a variety of purposes. These purposes include training, self-assessment, quality system development, quality improvement, and strategic planning.

---

*Published by the United States Department of Commerce. This material is not published under copyright.

Key concepts in the award examination criteria

The Award Examination is built upon a number of key concepts. Together, these concepts underlie all requirements included in the Examination Items.

- Quality is defined by the customer.
- The senior leadership of businesses needs to create clear quality values and build the values into the way the company operates.
- Quality excellence derives from well-designed and well-executed systems and processes.
- Continuous improvement must be part of the management of all systems and processes.
- Companies need to develop goals, as well as strategic and operational plans to achieve quality leadership.
- Shortening the response time of all operations and processes of the company needs to be part of the quality improvement effort.
- Operations and decisions of the company need to be based upon facts and data.
- All employees must be suitably trained and developed and involved in quality activities.
- Design quality and defect and error prevention should be major elements of the quality system.
- Companies need to communicate quality requirements to suppliers and work to elevate supplier quality performance. Several of these concepts are described in greater detail below.

Customer-Driven Quality   Quality is judged by the customer. All product and service attributes that contribute value to the customer, lead to customer satisfaction, and affect customer preference must be addressed appropriately in quality systems. Value, satisfaction, and preference may be influenced by many factors throughout the overall purchase, ownership, and service experiences of customers. This includes the relationship between the company and customers—the trust and confidence in products and services—that leads to loyalty and preference. This concept of quality includes not only the product and service attributes that meet basic requirements. It also includes those that enhance them and differentiate them from competing offerings. Such enhancement and differentiation may include unique product-product, service-service, or product-service combinations. Customer-driven quality is thus a strategic concept. It demands constant sensitivity to customer and market information and rapid response to requirements. These requirements extend well beyond defect and error reduction, merely meeting specifications, or reducing complaints. Nevertheless, defect and error reduction and elimination of causes of dissatisfaction contribute significantly to the customers' view of quality and are thus also important parts of customer-driven quality.

    Leadership   A company's senior leaders must create clear quality values, specific goals, and well-defined systems and methods for achieving the goals. The systems and methods need to guide all activities of the company and encourage participation by all employees. Through their regular personal involvement in visible activities such as goal setting, planning, review of company quality performance, and recognizing employees for quality achievement, the senior leaders reinforce the values and encourage leadership in all levels of management.

Continuous improvement   Achieving the highest levels of quality and competitiveness requires a well-defined and well-executed approach to continuous improvement of all operations and of all work unit activities of a company. Improvements may be of several types: (1) enhancing value to the customer through improved product and service attributes; (2) reducing errors and defects; (3) improving responsiveness and cycle time performance; and (4) improving efficiency and effectiveness in use of all resources. Thus, improvement is driven not only by the objective to provide superior quality. It is driven also by the need to be responsive and efficient—both conferring additional marketplace advantages. To meet all of these requirements, the process of continuous improvement must contain regular cycles of planning, execution, and evaluation. It must be accompanied by a basis—preferably a quantitative basis—for assessing progress, and for deriving information for future cycles of improvement.

Fast response   Meeting customer requirements and expectations and success in competitive markets increasingly demand ever shorter product and service introduction cycles and more rapid response to customers. Indeed, fast response itself is often a major quality attribute. Reduction in cycle times and lead times and rapid response to customers can occur only when quality systems and processes are designed to meet both quality and response goals and when response time is included as a major focus of quality improvement processes. This requires that all designs, objectives, and work unit activities include measurement and monitoring of cycle time and responsiveness to seek opportunities for improvement. Major gains in response may occur when work processes and paths are simplified and shortened. Such improvements are often accompanied by simultaneous improvements in quality. Hence it is highly beneficial to consider response time and quality together.

Actions based on facts, data, and analysis   Meeting quality improvement goals of the company requires that actions in setting, controlling, and changing systems and processes be based upon reliable information, data, and analysis. Facts and data needed for quality assessment and quality improvement are of many types, including: customer, product and service performance, operations, market, competitive comparisons, supplier, and employee-related. Analysis refers to the process of extraction of larger meaning from data to support evaluation and decision making at various levels within the company. Such analysis may entail using data individually or in combination to reveal information—such as trends, projections, and cause and effect—that might not be evident without analysis. Facts, data, and analysis support a variety of company purposes, such as planning, reviewing company performance, improving operations, and comparing company quality performance with competitors.

A major consideration relating to data and analysis in connection with quality system development, competitive performance, and continuous improvement involves the creation and use of performance indicators. Performance indicators are measurable characteristics of products, services, processes, and operations the company uses to evaluate performance and to track progress. The indicators should be selected to best represent the attributes that link to customer requirements, customer satisfaction, and competitive performance as well as to operational effectiveness and efficiency. A system of indicators thus represents a clear and objective basis for aligning all activities of the company toward well-defined goals and for tracking progress toward the goals. Through the analysis of data obtained in the tracking processes, the indicators themselves may be evaluated and changed. For example, indicators selected to measure product and service quality may be judged by how well they correlate with customer satisfaction.

Participation by all employees   Meeting the company's quality objectives requires a fully committed, well-trained work force that is encouraged to participate in the company's continuous improvement activities. Reward and recognition systems need to reinforce participation and emphasize achievement of quality objectives. Factors bearing upon the safety, health, well-being, and morale of employees need to be part of the continuous improvement objectives and activities of the company. Employees need to receive training in basic quality skills related to performing their work and to understanding and solving quality-related problems.

Examination categories, items, and point values

1991 Examination Categories/Items

	Maximum Points	
1.0 Leadership	100	
1.1 Senior Executive Leadership		40
1.2 Quality Values		15
1.3 Management for Quality		25
1.4 Public Responsibility		20
2.0 Information and Analysis	70	
2.1 Scope and Management of Quality Data and Information		20
2.2 Competitive Comparisons and Benchmarks		30
2.3 Analysis of Quality Data and Information		20
3.0 Strategic Quality Planning	60	
3.1 Strategic Quality Planning Process		35
3.2 Quality Goals and Plans		25
4.0 Human Resource Utilization	150	
4.1 Human Resource Management		20
4.2 Employee Involvement		40
4.3 Quality Training and Education		40
4.4 Employee Recognition and Performance Measurement		25
4.5 Employee Well-Being and Morale		25
5.0 Quality Assurance of Products and Services	140	
5.1 Design and Introduction of Quality Products and Services		35
5.2 Process Quality Control		20
5.3 Continuous Improvement of Processes		20

Key business factors

Below is a summary by Examination Category of how key business factors are taken into account in evaluation.

Leadership   This category examines the senior executives' leadership in creating quality values, building the values into the way the company does business, and how the executives and the company project the quality values outside the company. Participation in activities such as those of national and international organizations and other activities given in this category depends upon the type of resources of the business, and its overall competitive and regulatory environments. Evaluations are based upon the appropriateness, effectiveness, and extent of the executives' and of the company's involvement in relation to the size and type of business. Whether or not the company has a quality department or officer, or regulatory affairs office or officer is not considered in the evaluation.

Information and analysis   This category examines the scope, validity, and use of data to determine the adequacy of the data system to support total quality management. The scope, management, and analysis of data depend upon the type of business, its resources, number and geographical distribution of business units, and other factors. Evaluations are based upon the appropriateness and effectiveness of methods for management of data [and] information and analysis of technology in relation to these business factors. Evaluations do not depend upon how activities are organized or whether or not the company has an information department or officer, or uses particular technologies to analyze data or to make data available throughout the company.

Strategic quality planning   This category examines the company's approach to planning to determine its adequacy to achieve or sustain quality leadership. While the planning processes and priority development do not depend appreciably upon the size and type of business, the scope and type of benchmark and competitive data may depend upon such business factors. Competitive and benchmark data are essential for planning quality leadership because they make possible clear and objective quality comparisons. The principal considerations in assessing the effectiveness of competitive and benchmark data are in relation to the competitive environment and resources of the company. However, if a company operates in a local or regional market, and there are other, non-competing companies in similar markets elsewhere, the company would be expected to reach beyond its local or regional market for competitive and benchmark data on key product, process, and service features.

Evaluations of planning are based upon the thoroughness and effectiveness of processes including the information used. Evaluations do not depend upon how planning activities are organized or whether or not the company has a planning department or officer.

Human resource utilization   This category examines the company's efforts to develop and involve the entire work force in total quality. The organization of efforts to develop and involve employees depends upon the number of employees, resources of the company, the geographical distribution of business units, and other factors. Evaluations depend upon the appropriateness and effectiveness of approaches to human resource development and do not depend upon whether or not the company has either a human resource department or officer, or training and education specialists or facilities. For example, education and training might be accomplished in a variety of ways such as through schools, contract, or through training given by customers.

Quality assurance of products and services   This category has a very strong process and systems orientation throughout. Processes may be carried out entirely by employees, largely by means of technology, or through a combination of the two. The degree of formality in systems and processes depends upon a number of factors such as size of the business, types of products and services, customer and government requirements, regulatory requirements, and number of business locations. Evaluations take into account consistency of execution of quality operations that incorporate a sound prevention basis accompanied by continuous quality improvement activities. Consistency of execution is taken to mean the existence of defined, suitably recorded processes with clear delineation of responsibilities. Evaluations do not depend upon how responsibilities are distributed or organized or whether or not the company has a quality organization or officer. Moreover, in small businesses, one person might carry out two or more functions.

Quality results   This category examines the company's quality improvement and quality levels by themselves and in relation to those of competitors. Included are quality of products and services, internal operations, and suppliers. The number and type of measures depend upon factors such as the company's size, types of products and services, and competitive environment. Evaluations take such factors into account and consider whether or not the measures are sufficient to support overall improvement and to establish clear quality levels and comparisons.

Customer satisfaction   This category examines the company's knowledge of customer requirements, service and responsiveness, and satisfaction results measured through a variety of indicators. The scope and organization of activities to gather information, to serve, and to respond to customers depend upon many factors such as company resources, types of products and services, and geographical distribution of business units and customers. Evaluations are based upon the appropriateness and effectiveness of efforts in relation to these business factors. They also take into account whether or not a company utilizes all instruments at its disposal or within its resources to meet all the key requirements of an excellent customer service system. Evaluations do not depend upon how responsibilities are distributed or whether or not the company has separate departments for customer service, complaints, or other special purposes.

Appendix C

The Total Quality Management action plan

A TQM action plan is one of the keys to the TQM process. The TQM action plan is continuous, detailed planning and actions focused on victory. It must be part of the organization's way of life. The plan gears the entire organization toward the critical processes required to achieve customer satisfaction.

TQM action plan outline

An outline of a TQM action plan is presented in this appendix. Any organization can write a TQM action plan for its specific vision. Victory can only be achieved by action. An entire organization's actions must be geared to victory.

Covers

The front cover should include the vision statement. The back cover might include the objectives of the organization.

Part 1 General

Section 1 Introduction

Contained in the introduction is a statement of what TQM is and how TQM will be used throughout the organization to meet strategic plans.

Section 2 TQM policy

This section should provide a clear, concise statement of the organization's TQM policy. It should also outline broad guidelines for action.

Section 3 Purpose of the TQM action plan

The purpose of the TQM action plan should be stated.

Section 4 TQM action plan process

Detailed guidance on the TQM action planning process should be provided. Specific procedures for using action planning as a living document throughout the organization should be outlined and explained.

Section 5 TQM terms

A list of TQM terms and definitions would be beneficial to foster understanding throughout the organization.

Part 2 Vision, objectives, goals, strategy, tactics and operations

Section 1 Vision

This section presents the vision statement, along with specific guidance for making the vision a reality.

Section 2 Objectives

Specific objectives for meeting the vision must be described.

Section 3 Goals

The TQM goals must be provided to ensure desired results.

Section 4 Strategy

A TQM strategy for achieving the goals must be given in this section.

Section 5 Tactics

The specific method of employing the organization to achieve the strategy should be defined.

Section 6 Operations

This section outlines the actions for each part of the organization to make the vision real.

Part 3 Involvement

Section 1 Introduction

This section provides an overview of involvement in the TQM process. It explains the involvement of employees, the specific use of teams, and supplier and customer involvement.

Section 2 Employee involvement

A clearly detailed description of what is expected from all employees should be presented in this section. This should include not only the expected employee's involvement in the performance of specific work but also improvement effort expectations.

Section 3 Team involvement

This section describes the use of teams in the TQM process.

Section 4 Suppliers involvement

Supplier involvement activities are detailed in this section.

Section 5 Customer involvement

This section discusses ways the organization fosters customer relationships and reinforces the focus on customer satisfaction.

Part 4 Continuous improvement system

Section 1 Introduction

The purpose of this section is to provide an overview of the continuous improvement system for the organization. It should outline in general terms the specific methodologies and tools and techniques used throughout the organization for continuous improvement.

Section 2 Disciplined methodology for continuous improvement

This section describes the specific methodology used throughout the organization for continuous improvement. It includes methods for improving processes, measuring performance, and solving problems.

Section 3 Systems improvements

Specific improvement systems being used for design, manufacturing, inventory reduction, and so on, should be identified in this section.

Section 4 Tools and techniques

A description of the TQM tools and techniques should be an integral part of the plan. In addition, specific guidance on the application of specific tools and techniques might be appropriate.

Part 5 Training, education, and career advancement

Section 1 Training

This section must detail specific training for the performance of current and future work in the organization. Such training could include training for job skills, TQM tools and technique skills, and/or team skills.

Section 2 Education

This section should describe specific educational requirements and development opportunities.

Section 3 Career advancement

A career advancement ladder outlining both education and training requirements should be provided to foster the lifelong learning process.

Part 6 Ownership and responsibilities

Section 1 Managers/leaders

This section gives the specific responsibilities of all managers and leaders.

Section 2 Employee

Employee responsibilities for job performance and improvement efforts should be explained. Detailed involvement, participation, and empowerment expectations must be described.

Section 3 Teams

The organization's use of teams should be described in this section.

Part 7 Reward and recognition

This part must fully describe the specific rewards and recognition systems within the organization. It should give details of all tangible and intangible rewards available.

Rewards should be tied to individual performance, skills, and knowledge; team performance; and impact on customer satisfaction.

Part 8 Support

Part 8 describes the support system. It must also detail the resources including funding.

The following support system elements should be addressed:

- Coach
- Steering Group
- Teams
- Mentor
- Owner
- Lead teams
- Facilitator
- Trainers

Part 9 Actions

This part provides the focus for action in the organization, and it does this by including all of the measurements of all critical processes in the organization. Reporting procedures should be included. This part should give the process, the owner, the measurement, how the process is performing in relationship to the goal, and the current status of all improvement efforts. For example, the report may be structured as follows:

Process	Owner	Current performance	Goal	Date

Part 10 Action plan appendices

Each organization within the overall organization should develop and maintain an appendix to the TQM action plan. All of these appendices should state specific goals and the measurements used to achieve these goals. Thus, each appendix should mirror the information used by the overall organization but tailor the information to one specific organization. Appendixes include:

Section 1   General
Section 2   Vision, objectives, goals, strategy, tactics, and operations
Section 3   Involvement
Section 4   Continuous improvement system
Section 5   Training, education, and career advancement
Section 6   Ownership and responsibilities
Section 7   Rewards and recognition
Section 8   Support
Section 9   Actions

Appendix D

Lessons learned

This appendix describes some of the lessons learned in implementing the TQM process. Although success in TQM cannot be guaranteed, sometimes it helps to learn from the mistakes of others. It is important not to be discouraged by occasional failures but to do everything possible to avoid catastrophic errors. The following are some of the errors to avoid and lessons learned from implementing TQM.

Lesson 1   Expecting results too quickly

The implementation of TQM does give some immediate results. However, the big payoff requires commitment and support for many years. The greatest benefits of TQM come when TQM is institutionalized. This might take many years to achieve.

Lesson 2   Copying from other organizations

Although learning from the successes and failures of other organizations is beneficial, the real success from TQM comes from the persistent application of the TQM philosophy and guiding principles in each organization's specific environment. Victory is different for each organization. It cannot be achieved by simply copying others.

Lesson 3   Starting with insufficient resources to create a TQM environment

Victory requires the full support and commitment of the entire organization. This requires resources that include funds, manpower, facilities, training, support structure, and in some cases technology.

Lesson 4   Thinking training is all that is required

Training and education are important elements of victory, but training alone will not give success. All the elements of victory are needed for TQM.

Lesson 5 Setting goals that are not attainable

Goals are essential to focus the organization on victory. People strive to achieve challenging goals, but no one wants to pursue unrealistic goals. Frequently, organizations initially set goals beyond their reach. The organization should set realistic goals and build on their successes. Remember, small successes repeated over and over build to big victories.

Lesson 6 Trying to solve the biggest problem all at once

TQM is based on achieving many small successes over time. Many of the problems of organizations have evolved over many years; they cannot all be solved at one time. Although it is important to focus improvement efforts on critical issues, make improvements little by little until these major issues are resolved. Tackling the biggest problem all at once only results in frustration and failure.

Lesson 7 Running TQM like a program

TQM is a way of life; it is not a program. TQM requires many changes in behavior that cannot be demanded. The goal of TQM is to institutionalize the philosophy and guiding principles as part of the organization. This can be accomplished only by continuous actions that reinforce TQM behaviors.

Lesson 8 Implementing only some of the elements of victory

All of the elements of victory are necessary. Some organizations pick and choose certain elements, expecting results. This will not work. The Victory-C approach of this book, which contains the elements of victory, can be found at the end of Appendix A.

Lesson 9 Lacking integrity, ethics, and trust

Integrity, ethics, and trust are the foundation of TQM. Integrity, ethics, and trust must be ingrained into the organizational environment in order to achieve victory.

Lesson 10 Lacking a vision that cannot be made real

A clear vision that can be made real by the organization is of primary importance for victory. Without a mission, the organization cannot start toward success. Also, the vision must be understood by the people who must make it happen. Everyone in the organization must see how they contribute to victory.

Lesson 11 Lacking an overall plan

The creation and maintenance of TQM requires an overall plan. TQM does not just happen. A systematic, integrated, consistent, organization-wide approach is necessary. This can only be achieved through complete planning.

Lesson 12 Paying lip service to improvement efforts

Making Total Quality Management a way of life in order to achieve victory takes more than words; it requires action. Action is needed to ensure the necessary TQM environment with all the elements of victory focused on customer satisfaction.

Lesson 13 Practicing policies and procedures that do not support the TQM environment

All the policies and procedures in the organization must reinforce the TQM environment to ensure the TQM way of life. For instance, compensation policies should reward TQM behavior. Procedures should allow people ownership of their work.

Lesson 14   Failing to communicate successes

In an organization, TQM spreads by word of mouth. TQM successes should be constantly visible to everyone. This helps the organization build on successes for the future.

Lesson 15   Preaching one thing but doing another

TQM can be established and maintained only by the action and example of the leadership. The leadership must consistently display the behaviors expected in a TQM environment.

Lesson 16   Failing to provide timely training

TQM requires training when it is needed to accomplish the improvement effort. Training should be geared to the specific improvement effort in question. All personnel on a team should go through the training together for each specific improvement effort. In addition, the training must be given to provide the skills for the improvement effort. These skills must be given just in time to accomplish necessary actions.

Lesson 17   Thinking once trained, always trained

Training must be continuously pursued.

Lesson 18   Failing to train, not simply educate, top leadership in TQM

Top leadership must thoroughly understand the TQM philosophy and guiding principles and their application, as well as the continuous improvement system and TQM tools and techniques, before attempting to start organization-wide training for other members of the organization.

Lesson 19   Feeling powerless to do anything

You can accomplish many improvements within your organization, department, function, section, team, and yourself where you do have control. Do whatever you can do; fix what you can. Remember, success breeds success. Your little improvements will lead to other little improvements, which will encourage others to make improvements. Little victories lead to big victories.

Lesson 20   Failing to communicate the meaning of TQM ownership

People need to understand the meaning of ownership in their organization. Frequently management suddenly announces that all people in the organization now have ownership of their work. Most people have no idea what this means. Ownership must be defined by the amount of responsibility and authority given to the people. An understanding of the meaning of ownership within the specific organization is essential to victory.

Lesson 21   Implementing continuous improvement in only one area

Many organizations focus their improvement effort on one or two areas without involvement of other essential functions. For instance, the improvement effort typically starts in the manufacturing, engineering, or human resources areas. It is necessary, however to ensure that the TQM environment and approach in time pervades the entire organization.

Lesson 22 Failing to balance short-term goals with long-term objectives

TQM requires a long-term perspective. Strive for short-term success focused on the long-term future of the organization. Many organizations are geared only to short-term gains or profits.

Lesson 23 Thinking technology is more important than people

Technology and people must be balanced in a TQM organization. Although technology lends definite advantages, people adding value is a primary principle of TQM. People are the most important resource.

Lesson 24 Failing to listen

Listening is a key element of communication in TQM. This is one of the major lessons learned. Victory requires listening to the people in the organization, the suppliers, and the customers.

Appendix E

Ethics: The foundation of Total Quality Management

This book has stressed again and again that TQM involves everyone in the goal of satisfying the customer. TQM has been presented as a philosophy and set of principles; tools and techniques to implement TQM have been introduced; and, the total TQM environment concepts have been presented more than once. However, the true foundation of TQM lies deeper than these concepts: it is integrity, ethics, and trust.

Any discussion of TQM that does not include a presentation of integrity and ethics would be greatly remiss; in fact, it would be incomplete. If victory is to be achieved, integrity, ethics, and trust must be a vital part of TQM.

As outlined in this book, TQM requires the active participation of everyone in the organization, and business is maintained and won through customer satisfaction. It is not achieved by bad business practices. This demands that everyone in the organization must have the highest standards of integrity, ethics, and trust in dealing with both internal and external customers. These three characteristics move together through the TQM environment. However, each element offers something different to the TQM concept.

Integrity

Integrity encompasses honesty, morality, values, fairness, factuality, and sincerity. Everyone in the organization and the customer, internal as well as external, expects and deserves to be treated with integrity.

The opposite of integrity is duplicity. TQM does not work in an atmosphere of duplicity. In an environment of deception, an organization takes actions that are contrary to the philosophy and guiding principles of TQM. If anyone in the organization perceives errant thought or action, active involvement will not be accomplished. In addition, if the customer perceives that the organization is guilty of duplicity, customer satisfaction will not be achieved, and quite likely the customer's business will be lost.

Ethics

Ethics is the discipline concerned with good and bad in any situation. Ethics is a two-faceted subject, represented by organizational and individual ethics.

In the case of organizational ethics, most organizations establish a business code of ethics outlining ethical guidelines that all employees are to adhere to in the performance of their work.

Individual ethics include personal rights or wrongs. They are concerned with legal, moral, and contractual business policies and individual dealings. A person should never do anything that goes against organizational standards or that the person would not like done to himself.

Trust

Trust is a by-product of integrity and ethical conduct. It is absolutely essential for the success of TQM. Trust is important in all aspects of TQM, including teamwork, improvement efforts and customer satisfaction. It is necessary to ensure, first, the full participation of all members on a team; second, a focus on improvement of processes, are not the control of people; and third, customer satisfaction.

Trust must be developed to remove the traditional conflicts in an organization. It can change the adversarial relationships between management and labor and between different functions in the organization. Trust builds the cooperative environment essential for TQM.

Key points

- Integrity, ethics, and trust are the foundation of Total Quality Management.
- Integrity is required in all dealings with both internal and external customers.
- Honesty, fairness, factual reporting, sincerity, loyalty, respect for others, and accountability are all necessary in a TQM environment.
- Neither the organization nor the individual should do anything that it would not want done to it.
- Trust is necessary to break the traditional barriers to cooperation—cooperation that is required in a TQM environment.

Appendix F

Fundamental statistics concepts for Total Quality Management

This appendix provides some of the basic statistics concepts applicable to a Total Quality Management organization. The purpose is to highlight some of the more important statistical concepts used with the many quantitative methods outlined in this field manual. Specific application of the statistical concepts within a Total Quality Management environment requires further, in-depth study.

Statistics is an essential element of Total Quality Management. TQM uses quantitative methods to improve continuously all the processes in the organization aimed at total customer satisfaction. This involves monitoring, analyzing, correcting, and improving processes using rational decision making based on statistics. Statistics plays a substantial role in a total quality environment. It is used for many purposes, including problem solving, process analysis, and pass/fail decisions. In problem solving, statistics helps in understanding the problem by determining actual performance, focusing on the vital few problems, and targeting the root causes. In process analysis, statistics assists in determining the performance and causes of variation in a process. Once the process performance is known, process improvement goals can be determined. In addition, variations in the process can be analyzed to determine the cause—common or special. The corrective action can be doing nothing, eliminating or reducing as much as possible the variation in the process, or improving the process. The first option should always be considered. When a chance variation of a process is discovered, this option is often overlooked, frequently resulting in a correction that only increases the variation. Next, eliminate special causes. Then, reduce common causes. Finally, focus on continuous process improvement. In pass/fail decisions, statistics can provide the criteria for the decision.

In order to use quantitative methods in the Total Quality Management environment, you need to understand some fundamental concepts of statistics. This appendix describes the following basics of statistics: population, sample, types of sampling, central limit theorem, types of data, data arrangement, measures of central tendencies, frequency distribution, normal distribution, variation, and process control.

Population and sample

The terms *population* and *sample* describe the relative data for the statistics. A population is a collection of all the data for a specific statistic. A sample is a collection of some of the data from a total population for a specific statistic. For instance, the test of all of the power supplies for a particular output after assembly is a test of the entire population. A test of only some of the power supplies for a particular output is a sample.

Types of sampling

There are two common types of samples, nonrandom and random. Nonrandom sampling is accomplished using judgment. This type of sample cannot usually be verified. In a TQM environment, nonrandom sampling is only recommended as a predecessor to random sampling. In random sampling, each item in the population has a chance of being selected. This type of sampling is more useful in a TQM environment; it ensures accurate statistics. Two of the most common forms of random sampling are simple random sampling and stratified sampling.

    Simple random sampling   Simple random sampling can be accomplished by using a list of random digits or slips. The random digit method uses a number to represent the items in the population. For instance, imagine the population consists of 100 items. The items are numbered 1 to 100. Next, the sample must be selected. The sample is selected by the use of a random number generator or a table of random digits. Suppose the sample consists of 10 items. The random number generator or table of random digits selects 10 items indiscriminately. With the slip method, each item in the population is also numbered. The numbers are recorded on slips, and the slips are put in a box. The sample is drawn from the slips in the box. These random sampling tools ensure that the sample represents the population so that inferences can then be made about the entire population.

    Stratified sampling   Stratified sampling divides the population into similar groups or strata. There are two methods of stratified sampling. One is to select at random a certain number of items from each group/stratum according to the proportion of the group/stratum to the population. With the other method, a certain number of items are selected from each group/stratum; then the group/stratum is given weight according to its proportion to the population.

The central limit theorem

The central limit theorem states: the mean (average) of the sampling distribution of the mean equals the population mean (average), regardless of sample size, and as the sample size increases, the sampling distribution of the mean approaches normal, regardless of the shape of the population. The central limit theorem allows the use of sample statistics to make judgments about the population of the statistic.

The central limit theorem is an important concept in statistics because it is often impractical or impossible to check the entire population.

Types of data

The two types of data are variable data and attribute data. Variable data measures characteristics having a range of values, that is, quality characteristics such as thickness, width, and temperature. Attribute data is associated with characteristics such as pass/fail, have/have not, go/no go, and accept/reject.

Data arrangement

Once you have collected the data from the population or sample, you must arrange it in a meaningful way. Arranging data allows you to observe such things as the highest and lowest values, trends, central tendencies, patterns, most common values, special causes, common causes, and so forth. The arrangement of data helps to determine the measures of central tendency and the frequency distribution.

Measure of central tendencies   The measures of central tendencies are mean, media, and mode. The mean is the average. The median is the middle value. The mode is the value most often represented in the data.

Example   The sample data is as shown. Column 1 is the number of the sample. Column 2 is the ages of the people in the sample as collected. Column 3 is sample data arranged lowest to highest.

Column 1	Column 2	Column 3
1.	30	30
2.	33	33
3.	42	35
4.	39	36
5.	50	39
6.	42	42
7.	35	42
8.	47	47
9.	36	49
10.	49	50

The average is calculated by summing all the items (in column 3) dividing the sum by the total number of items, as follows:

$$\text{Mean} = \frac{30 + 33 + 36 + 39 + 42 + 42 + 47 + 49 + 50}{10}$$

$$= \frac{403}{10}$$

$$= 40.3$$

The median is the central item in a set of data. Half of the items fall above the median, and half of the items fall below it. In the example above, the median is 40.5.

$$\text{Median} = \frac{39 + 42}{2}$$

$$= 40.5$$

Mode is the value that is most often repeated in a set of data. In the example, the mode is 42.

Frequency distribution   A frequency distribution is a table showing the number of elements in each class of a set of data. In it, the data is arranged into classes with the number of observations in each class. A class is a group of data that describes one characteristic of the data. A frequency distribution displays the number of times an observation of the characteristic falls into each class.

Example   The first step in constructing a frequency diagram is to collect the data. The raw data for the average inventory of work in process for one assembly area over a 15-day period is as follows:

1 1 5 2 4 3 3 1 2 3 3 4 3 2 3

The second step is to arrange the data from lowest to highest:

1 1 1 2 2 2 3 3 3 3 3 3 4 4 5

In third step, determine class intervals. The class intervals should be equal. One method for determining class intervals is to subtract the lowest value from the highest value and divide by the number of classes. For the example, the formula provides a class interval. This gives the following class levels:

1	1.8
1.9	2.7
2.8	3.6
3.7	4.5
4.6	5.3

Next, sort the data into classes and count the number of points.

		Count
1	1.8	3
1.9	2.7	3
2.8	3.6	6
3.7	4.5	2
4.6	5.3	1

Then, determine the relative frequency and/or cumulative frequency of the data. The following array shows relative frequency and cumulative frequency of the data.

		Count	Relative	Cumulative
1	1.8	3	20	20
1.9	2.7	3	20	20
2.8	3.6	6	40	80
3.7	4.5	2	13	93
4.6	5.3	1	7	100
		15	100	100

Finally, display the data on a histogram chart, as shown in chapter 9.

Normal distribution

Normal distribution is shown as a bell-shaped curve, as illustrated in FIG. F-1. In a normal distribution, the mean, median, and mode are equal.

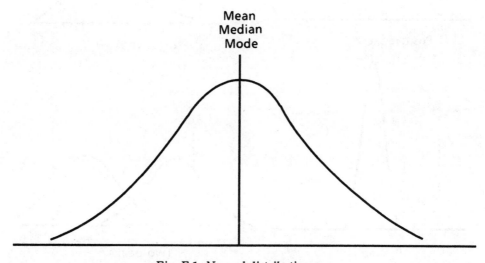

Fig. F-1. Normal distribution curve.

Variation

Variation is any deviation from the best target value. Variation is shown by spread (dispersion), shape (skewness), and peak (hurtosis). The spread shows the variability about the target, the shape indicates abnormalities, and the peak displays the closeness to the aim of the process. Figure F-2 shows some distributions. These distribution charts indicate abnormalities (except for Normal Spread). Further, the charts indicate the appropriate action, if any, for correcting the process.

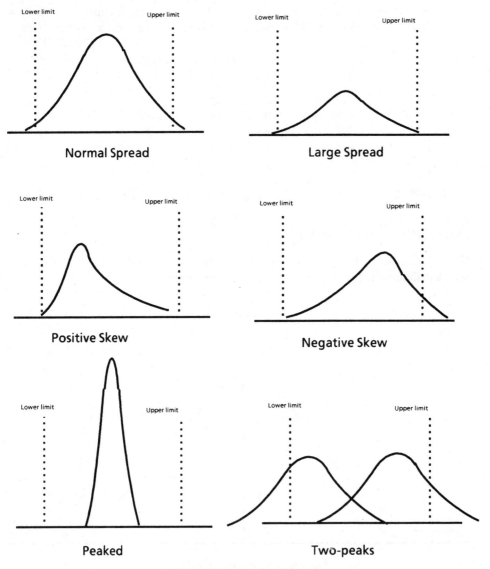

Fig. F-2. Examples of distribution.

Dispersion

The range, variance, and standard deviation are the most important measure of dispersion. They tell the distances of any observation in the data. The range shows the distance from lowest to the highest. The variance and standard deviation provide average distance of any data from the mean of the statistic.

Range   The range is the difference between the lowest and highest data points. The range is calculated by simply subtracting the lowest value from the highest value.

Variance   The variance is the average squared distance between the mean and each item. The formulas for computing the population and sample variance are as follows:

Population

$$\sigma^2 = \frac{\Sigma (X - \mu)^2}{N}$$

where

σ^2 = Population variance
X = Value of observation in the population
μ = Mean of the population
N = Number of total observations in the population

Sample

$$s^2 = \frac{\Sigma (X - \overline{X})^2}{n - 1}$$

where

s^2 = Sample variance
X = Value of observation in the sample
$\overline{X}$ = Mean of the sample
n = Number of observations in the sample

Standard deviation   The standard deviation is the square root of the average of the squared distances between the mean and each item. The standard deviation is the square root of the variance. The formulas for calculating the population and sample standard deviation are as follows:

Population

$$\sigma = \sqrt{\frac{\Sigma (X - \mu)^2}{N}}$$

where

σ = Population standard variance
X = Value of observation in the population
μ = Mean of the population
N = Number of total observations in the population

Sample

$$s = \sqrt{\frac{\Sigma\,(X - \overline{X})^2}{n-1}}$$

where

    s = Sample variance
    X = Value of observation in the population
    $\overline{X}$ = Mean of the sample
    n = Number of observations in the sample

Standard deviation in a normal curve The standard deviation in a normal curve allows precise measurement of the percentage of items that fall within a specific range. Figure F-3 shows the percentages of items within specific ranges of the standard deviation. Under normal curve, the percentage of items that fall within a certain number of standard deviations is as follows:

1. 68.28% of the values are ±1 standard deviation.
2. 95.46% of the values are ±2 standard deviations.
3. 97.73% of the values fall within ±3 standard deviations.

STANDARD DEVIATION

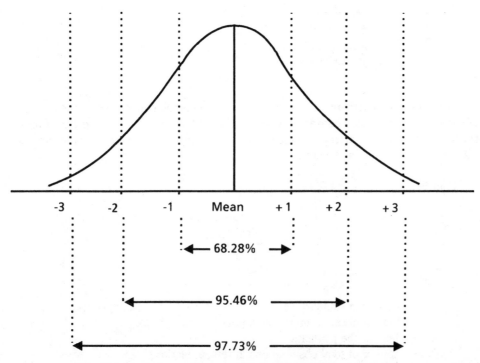

Fig. F-3. Percentage of items within specific standard deviations.

Process control

Process control is normally accomplished using statistical process control (SPC) techniques. Specific statistical process control techniques are beyond the scope of this book. However, sources at the end of this book give detailed information on statistical process control. Two of the fundamental concepts of statistical process control are control charts and process capability indexes.

Control charts

Control charts monitor processes. These charts assist in determining in-control and out-of-control conditions. There are many types of control charts; the specific chart used depends on the purpose and type of data.

Some of the types of control charts include mean (average) charts (X bar), range charts (R), standard deviation charts, percent defect charts (p and p bar), defects-per-unit chart (u), and defects-per-sample charts (c). Mean charts, range charts, and standard deviation charts are usually used for measuring variable data, and percent defect charts, defects-per-unit charts, and defects-per-sample charts are used for attribute data. A control chart consists of a center line and the statistical control limits. The center line is the mean. The statistical control limits are usually ±3 standard deviations (sigma). As shown in FIG. F-4, the upper control limit is +3σ (sigma) of the process, and the lower control limit is −3σ of the process.

Besides indicating an in-control or out-of-control process, control charts also provide information on abnormalities, trends, and cycles. An abnormality exists when the data shows consistent data either above or below the center line. A trend is displayed by a constant increase or decrease in the data values. Cycles are recurring patterns of the data.

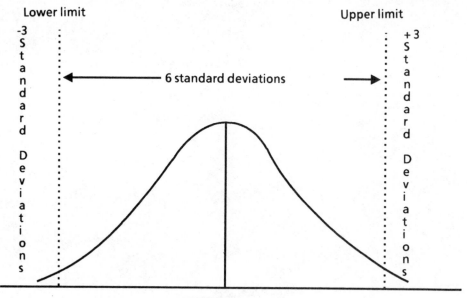

Fig. F-4. Control limits.

Process capability indexes

Process capability indexes provide an indication of the performance of a process. Two of the most common process capability indexes are the CP and CPK indexes. The CP index gives the ratio of the specification limits to the process limits. This helps determine whether the process is capable of producing within the specification. The objective is a CP greater than or equal to 1. CPK is the location of the process range within the specification limits. This index provides evidence that the product meets the specification. The objective of CPK is greater than or equal to 1. The process is centered when the CPK and CP equals 1. This indicates a capable process.

Glossary

activities   The steps of a process.

agenda   A plan for conducting a meeting.

appraisal costs   Costs associated with inspecting a product to ensure that it meets the customer's needs and expectation.

augmented product   A product that offers more than the customer is accustomed to expect.

bar chart   A chart for comparing many events or items.

benchmarking   A method of measuring an organization against those of recognized leaders or the best of class.

best of class   One of a group of similar organizations whose overall performance, effectiveness, efficiency, and adaptability is superior to all others.

brainstorming   Technique that encourages the collective thinking power of a group to create ideas.

cause   The reason for an action or a condition.

cause-and-effect analysis   Technique for helping a group examine underlying causes; fishbone.

chart   A graphic picture of data that highlights important trends and significant relationships.

check sheet   A list made to collect data.

coach   Person who acts as a guide for an organization in creating and maintaining the Total Quality Management environment.

commitment   Personal resolve to do something.

common cause   Normal variation in an established process.

communication   Technique for exchanging information.

competition   Anyone or anything competing for total customer satisfaction.

Computer-Aided Acquisition and Logistics Support (CALS)   A strategy for instituting within DoD and industry an integrated "system of systems" to create, transmit, and use technical information in digital form to design, manufacture, and support weapon systems and equipment, and apply communication and computer technology to the acquisition and support of major weapon systems and information systems.

Computer-Aided Design (CAD)   Automated system for assisting in design process.

Computer-Aided Engineering (CAE) Automated system for assisting in engineering process.

Computer-Aided Manufacturing (CAM) Automated system for assisting process design for manufacturing.

Computer Integrated Manufacturing (CIM) The integration of computer-aided design and computer-aided manufacturing for all design and manufacturing processes.

computer systems Items such as hardware, software, firmware, robotics, expert systems, and artificial intelligence.

Concurrent Engineering (CE) Systematic approach to the integrated, concurrent design of products and their related processes, including manufacture and support. This approach is intended to cause the developers, from the outset, to consider all elements of the product life cycle from conception through disposal, including quality, cost, schedule, and user requirements.

consensus The agreement reached by everyone.

continuous improvement system A disciplined methodology to achieve the goal of commitment to excellence by continually improving all processes.

control chart A chart that shows process performance in relation to control limits.

corrective action An action used to correct an unwanted condition.

Cost Of Poor Quality (COPQ) Term for techniques that focus on minimizing the cost of nonconformance.

Cost Of Quality (COQ) Term for techniques used to identify the cost of conformance and nonconformance. This includes the costs of prevention, appraisal, and failure.

criterion A standard on which a decision can be based.

culture A prevailing pattern of activities, interactions, norms, sentiments, beliefs, attitudes, values, and products in an organization. The shared experience of a group.

customer Everyone affected by a product and/or service. The customer can be the ultimate user of the product and/or service, known as an external customer, or the next person or process in the organization, known as an internal customer.

customer logistics All elements of logistics focusing on customer satisfaction.

customer satisfaction In Total Quality Management, quality.

customer/supplier analysis Techniques that provide insight into the customer's needs and expectations and involve an organization's suppliers in the development of the organization's requirements and the suppliers' conformance to them.

cycle time The time from the beginning of a process to the end of a process.

data Information or a set of facts.

data/statistical analysis Tools for collecting, sorting, charting, and analyzing data to make decisions.

decision-making The process of making a selection.

defect Any state of nonconformance to requirements.

design of experiments Traditionally, an experimental tool used to establish both parametric relationships and a product/process model in the early (applied research) stages of the design process.

design phases   The three phases of the design of a product or process are, according to Taguchi, systems design, parameter design, and tolerance design.

detailed process diagram   A flowchart, consisting of symbols and words, that completely describes a process.

detection   Identification of nonconformance after the fact.

deviation   Any nonconformance to a standard or requirement.

disciplined continuous improvement methodology   The continuous improvement system.

driving forces   Those forces that are pushing toward the achievement of a goal.

economic war   A war based on the production, consumption, and distribution of goods and services for profit.

effect   A problem or defect that occurs on the specific job to which a group or team is assigned.

effectiveness   A characteristic used to describe a process in which output conforms to requirements.

efficiency   A characteristic used to describe a process that produces the required output at a perceived minimum cost.

empowerment   The power of people to do whatever is necessary to do the job and improve the system.

expected product   The customer's minimal expectations, which includes the generic product.

external customer   The ultimate user of the product and/or service.

extrinsic reward   A reward given by other people.

facilitator   One who assists the group or team in applying the TQM tools and techniques.

fishbone   See cause-and-effects analysis.

flow diagram   A drawing combined with words used for defining a process. This tool provides an indication of problem areas, unnecessary loops and complexity, non-value-added tasks, and areas where the simplification of a process is possible.

focus setting   Technique used to focus on a specific outcome.

force field analysis   Technique that helps a group or team describe the forces at work in a given situation.

functional organization   An organization responsible for a major organizational function, such as marketing, sales, design, manufacturing, or distribution.

functional team   A team consisting of representatives from only one functional area.

generic product   The basic item.

goal   The specific desired outcome.

group   In TQM, a team.

guideline   A suggested practice that is not mandatory in programs intended to comply with a standard.

hierarchical nature of a process   The various levels of a process.

histogram   A chart that shows frequency of data in column form.

House of Quality   Quality functional deployment planning chart.

human resources   The people in an organization.

improvement methodology A method for making improvements in an organization.

in-control process A process within the upper and lower limits.

individual involvement Involvement of each person in the output of the organization.

information system Automated systems used throughout the organization to review, analyze, and take corrective action.

In-plant Quality Evaluation program (IQUE) Method by which in-plant government personnel evaluate contractor controls over product quality.

input What is needed to do the job.

input/output analysis Technique for identifying interdependency problems.

institutionalize To make an integral part of an organization's way of life.

internal customer Next person or process in the organization. A person or process within the organization that functions as a customer.

intrinsic reward A reward that is an integral part of the system. A reward that is within the individual person.

just-in-time Method of having the right material at the right time to be used in an operation.

leadership Guidance of a group of people to accomplish a goal.

lead team A team that oversees several other teams.

life cycle cost The total cost of a system or item over its full lifetime, including the cost of acquisition, ownership, and disposal.

line chart A chart that describes and compares quantifiable information.

listening Technique for receiving and understanding information.

logistics The aspect of military science dealing with the procurement, maintenance, and transportation of materiel, facilities, and people.

loss function The function of an organization that examines the costs associated with any variation from the target value of a quality characteristic.

lower control limit The lower control limit of a process minus 3σ of the statistic.

maintenance The repair of an item.

Malcolm Baldrige National Quality Award An annual award created by public law to recognize U.S. companies that excel in achievement and management to help improve quality and productivity.

management The leadership of an organization.

Manufacturing Resource Planning II (MRPII) System for planning and controlling a manufacturing company's operation.

Mean The average of a group of data.

Mean Time Between Failures (MTBF) The average time between successive failures of a given product.

measurement The act or process of measuring in order to compare results with requirements. A quantitative estimate of performance.

meeting Technique of bringing people together in a group to work for a common goal.

mentor A person assigned as management interface support for a team.

mission The intended result.

mistake proofing Technique for avoiding simple, human error at work; poka yoke.

multifunctional team   A team consisting of representatives from more than one function.

noise   Disruption of a process or function.

Nominal Group Technique (NGT)   Technique similar to brainstorming that provides structured discussion and decision making.

non-value-added   Term used to describe a process, activity, or task that does not provide any value to the product.

out-of-control process   A process for which the outcome is unpredictable.

output   The results of a job.

owner   The person who can change the process without further approval.

ownership   The power to have control over; possessing the authority to carry out the required actions.

parameter (or robust) design   Design of product (or process) that makes the performance (or output) insensitive to variation by moving toward the best target values of quality characteristics.

parametric design   The design phase in which the sensitivity to noise, or the disruption of a function, is reduced.

Pareto's principle   The principle that a large percentage of the results are caused by a small percentage of the causes. For instance, 80 percent of results are caused by 20 percent of causes.

people involvement   Individual and group activities.

performance   A term used to describe both the work product itself and a general process characteristic. The broad performance characteristics that are of interest to management are quality (effectiveness), cost (efficiency), and schedule. Performance is the highly effective common measurement that links the quality of the work product to efficiency and productivity.

pie chart   A chart in circular form that is divided to show the relationship between items and the whole.

plan   A specified course of action designed to attain a stated objective.

poka yoke   See mistake proofing.

policy   A statement of principles and beliefs, or an adopted course, to guide the overall management of affairs in support of a stated aim or goal. It is largely related to fundamental conduct and usually defines a general framework within which other business and management actions are carried out.

population   A complete collection of items (product observations, data) about certain characteristics that is then used to make conclusions and decisions for the purpose of process assessment and quality improvement.

potential product   Anything that can be used to attract and hold customers beyond the augmented product.

presentation   Tool for providing information, gaining approval, or requesting action.

prevention   A future-oriented approach to quality management that achieves quality improvement through corrective action on a process.

prevention costs   Costs incurred in product or process planning to ensure that defects do not occur.

problem   A question or situation proposed for solution. A taste that is the result of nonconformance to requirements, in other words, a task resulting from the existence of defects.

process   A series of activities that takes an input, modifies the input (work takes place/value is added), and produces an output.

process analysis   Tool used to improve a process and reduce process time by eliminating non-value-added activities and/or simplifying the process.

process capability   Long-term performance level after a process has been brought under control.

process control   In statistics, the set of activities used to detect and remove special causes of variation in order to maintain or restore stability.

process design   The development of a process.

process diagram   A tool for defining a process.

process improvement   The set of activities used to detect and remove common causes of variation in order to improve process capability. Process improvement leads to quality improvement.

process improvement team   A team of employees with representative skills and functions chosen to work on a specific process or processes.

process logistics   All aspects of logistics within an organization.

process management   A management approach comprising quality management and process optimization.

process optimization   The major aspect of process management that concerns itself with the efficiency and productivity of the process, that is, economic factors.

process owner   A designated person within a process who has the authority to manage the process and is responsible for its overall performance.

process performance   A measure of the effectiveness and efficiency with which a process satisfies customer requirements.

process review   An objective assessment of the methodology applied to a process, with emphasis on the potential for long-term process results rather than the actual short-term results achieved.

product   An output of a process provided to an internal or external customer, including goods, systems, equipment, hardware, software, services, and information.

product design   The development of the product.

production process   The manufacture of the product.

productivity   The value added by the process divided by the value of the labor and capital consumed.

quality   In Total Quality Management, total customer satisfaction.

quality (DoD)   Conformance to a set of customer requirements that, if met, result in a product or service that is fit for its intended use.

quality (product)   Conformance to requirements.

quality (Taguchi)   The (measure of degree of) loss a product causes after being shipped, other than any losses caused by its intrinsic functions.

Quality Function Deployment (QFD)   A disciplined approach used to transform customer requirements (the voice of the customer) into product development requirements.

quality improvement team   A group of individuals charged with the responsibility of planning and implementing quality improvement.

quantitative methods   Use of measurements.

R&M 2000   The reliability and maintainability approach of the Department of Defense to increase combat capability by reducing costs through specific practices.

range   The difference between the maximum value and the minimum value of data in a sample.

recognition   Special attention paid to an individual or group.

reliability   The probability that an item will perform its intended function for a specified interval under stated conditions.

requirement   A formal statement of a particular need and the expected manner in which it is to be met.

requirements   Expectations for a product or service. The "it" in "Do it right the first time." Specific and measurable customer needs with an associated performance standard.

restraining forces   Forces that keep a situation from improving.

reward   Recompense, either external or internal. External rewards to an individual are controlled by other people; they are pay, promotion, and benefits. Internal rewards come from the task or individual; they include things such as a challenge, a feeling of accomplishment, a feeling of belonging, and a sense of pride.

robust design   The design of a product for minimal quality losses.

root cause   Underlying reason for nonconformance within a process. When it is removed or corrected, the nonconformance is eliminated.

rules of conduct   Rules that provide guidance for group or team conduct.

sample   A finite number of items taken from a population.

sampling   The collection of some, but not all, of the data.

scatter chart   A chart that depicts the relationship between two or more factors.

selection grid   Tool for comparing each problem, opportunity, or alternative against all others.

selection matrix   Technique for rating problems, opportunities, or alternatives based on specific criteria.

seven tools of quality   The seven tools are: Pareto charts, cause-and-effect diagrams, stratification, check sheet, histogram, scatter diagram, and Shewhart (Deming) cycle.

simulation   Technique of observing and manipulating an artificial mechanism (model) that represents a real-world process that, for technical or economical reasons, is not suitable or available for direct experimentation.

sorting   Arranging information in some order, such as in classes or categories.

special/assignable cause   An abnormal cause of variation in a process.

specification   A document containing a detailed description or enumeration of particulars. Formal description of a work product and the intended manner of providing it. (The provider's view of the work product.)

standard deviation   A parameter describing the spread of the process output. The positive square root of the variance.

statistic   Any parameter that can be determined on the basis of the quantitative characteristics of a sample.

statistical control   Term used to describe a process from which all special causes of variation have been removed, leaving only common causes. Such a process is also said to be stable.

statistical estimation   The analysis of a sample parameter for the purpose of predicting the values of the corresponding population parameter.

statistical methods   The application of the theory of probability to problems of variation.

Statistical Process Control (SPC)   Statistical tool for monitoring and controlling a process to maintain and possibly improve quality.

statistics   The branch of applied mathematics that describes and analyzes empirical observations for the purpose of predicting certain events in order to make decisions in the face of uncertainty.

steering group   An executive-level steering committee.

Strategic Total Quality Management Plan (STQMP)   The overall plan for creating and maintaining a TQM environment.

strategic Total Quality Management planning cycle   A plan consisting of several stages: defining the vision, determining strategic improvement opportunities, selecting strategic opportunities for improvement, developing and maintaining the TQM action plan using a disciplined methodology, evaluating results, and doing it over again in a never-ending cycle.

strategy   A broad course of action, chosen from a number of alternatives, to accomplish a stated goal in the face of uncertainty.

subprocesses   The internal processes that make up a process.

supplier   An individual, organization, or firm that provides inputs to a process. The supplier can be external or internal to a company, firm, or organization.

supplier/customer analysis   Technique used to obtain and exchange information for conveying an organization's needs and requirements to suppliers and mutually determining the needs and expectations of the customers.

supplier logistics   All the logistics inputs into an organization.

support system   A system within an organization that guides the organization through the TQM process.

system   Many processes combined to accomplish a specific function.

system improvement   A method that focuses on the development or redesign of systems.

systems (parts) or concept design   This design phase arrives at the design architecture (size, shape, materials, number of parts) by looking at the best available technology. In American usage, commonly called the parts design phase.

Taguchi approach   Techniques for reducing the variation of a product or process performance to minimize loss.

task   One of a number of actions required to complete an activity.

team   Group of people working together toward common goal.

teamwork   Shared responsibility for the completion of a task or problem.

tolerance design   A stage of design that focuses on setting tight tolerances to reduce variation in performance. Because it is the phase most responsible for adding costs, it is essential to reduce the need for setting tight tolerances by successfully producing robust products and processes in the earlier parameter design phase.

top-down process diagram   A chart of the major steps and substeps in a process.

top-level process diagram   A diagram of the entire, overall process.

total   Term used to describe the involvement of everyone and everything in a continuous improvement effort.

Total Customer Service   All the features, acts, and information that augment the customer's ability to realize the potential of the core product or service.

total integrated logistics   The integration of all the logistics elements involved in the inputs to the organization, all the processes within the organization, and the outputs of the organization to ensure total customer supportability at an optimal life cycle cost.

total product concept   A concept that provides an insight into the range of possibilities for a product. It includes the generic product, expected product, augmented product, and potential product.

total production maintenance   System for involving the total organization in maintenance activities.

Total Quality Management (TQM)   A philosophy and a set of guiding principles that represent the foundation of a continuously improving organization. TQM is the application of quantitative methods and human resources to improve the material services supplied to an organization, all the processes within the organization, and the degree to which the needs of the customer are met, now and in the future. TQM integrates fundamental management techniques, existing improvement efforts, and technical tools under a disciplined approach focused on continuous improvement.

Total Quality Management action planning   The specific road map for the overall TQM effort that establishes a clear focus for the organization.

Total Quality Management philosophy   The overall, general concepts for a continuously improving organization.

Total Quality Management principles   The essential fundamental rules required to achieve victory.

Total Quality Management process   The process that transforms all the inputs into the organization into a product and/or service that satisfies the customer, that is, the output.

Total Quality Management umbrella   The integration of all the fundamental management techniques, existing improvement efforts, and technical tools under a disciplined approach focused on continuous improvement.

trainers   People in an organization who provide TQM and job skills training.

training   The teaching of skills to accomplish actions.

upper control limit   The upper control limit of a process plus 3σ of the statistic.

value engineering   An organized effort directed at analyzing the function of systems, equipment, facilities, services, and supplies for the purpose of achieving essential functions at the lowest life cycle cost consistent with performance, reliability, maintainability, interchangeability, product quality, and safety.

variable   A data item that takes on values within some range with a certain frequency or pattern.

variance   In quality management terminology, any nonconformance to specifications, in statistics, the square of the standard deviation.

Victory-C TQM model A systematic, integrated, consistent, organization-wide model consisting of all the elements required for victory and focused on total customer satisfaction.

VICTORY elements

Vision and leadership
Involvement of everyone and everything
Continuous improvement of all systems and processes
Training and education
Ownership
Reward and recognition
Years of support and commitment from management

vision Where an organization wants to go, that is, what a particular organization perceives as victory.

vote Technique used to determine majority opinion.

Abbreviations and acronyms

CAD	Computer-Aided Design
CAE	Computer-Aided Engineering
CALS	Computer-Aided Acquisition and Logistics Support
CAM	Computer-Aided Manufacturing
CE	Concurrent Engineering
CIM	Computer Integrated Manufacturing
CIS	Continuous Improvement System
COPQ	Cost of Poor Quality
COQ	Cost of Quality
CS	Computer System
DAB	Defense Acquisition Board
DCIMI	Defense Council on Integrity and Management Improvement
DoD	Department of Defense
DOE	Design of Experiments
DSMC	Defense Systems Management College
ESC	Executive Steering Committee
FM&P	Funding, Manpower, and Personnel
ILS	Integrated Logistics Support
IQUE	In-Plant Quality Evaluation
IS	Information System
JIT	Just-in-time
LCC	Life Cycle Cost
LCL	Lower Control Limit
MBO	Management by Objectives
MRPII	Manufacturing Resource Planning II
MTBF	Mean Time Between Failures
NGT	Nominal Group Technique
NPRDC	Navy Personnel Research and Development Center
OFI	Opportunities for Improvement
OSD	Office of Secretary of Defense
P&L	Production and Logistics
PDCA	Plan, Do, Check, Act

PGC	Policy Guidance Council
QA	Quality Assurance
QFD	Quality Function Deployment
QMB	Quality Management Board
QPD	Quality Policy Deployment
R&D	Research and Development
R&M	Reliability and Maintainability
RD	Robust Design
SDRL	Subcontractor Data Requirement List
SPC	Statistical Process Control
SQI	Service Quality Indicator
STQM	Strategic Total Quality Management
STQMP	Strategic Total Quality Management Plan
T&E	Training and Education
TCS	Total Customer Service
TEMP	Test and Evaluation Master Plan
TIL	Total Integrated Logistics
TPM	Total Production Maintenance
TQM	Total Quality Management
UCL	Upper Control Limit
VE	Value Engineering

Sources of information

Books

Amsden, Robert T., Butler, Howard E., and Amsden, Davida M. *Statistical Process Control, Simplified*. White Plains, NY, Quality Resources, 1989.

Aubrey, Charles A. II and Felkins, Patricia K. *Teamwork: Involving People in Quality and Productivity Improvement*. Milwaukee, ASQC Quality Press, 1988.

Brassard, Michael. *The Memory Jogger Plus*. Methuen, MA, GOAL/QPC, 1989.

Camp, Robert C. *Benchmarking*. Milwaukee, ASQC Quality Press, 1989.

Clavell, James, Ed. *Art of War*. New York, Dell Publishing, 1983.

Crosby, Philip B. *Quality is Free*. New York, McGraw-Hill, Inc., 1979.

_____. *Running Things*. New York, McGraw-Hill, Inc., 1986.

Davidow, William H. and Uttal, Bro. *Total Customer Service*. New York, Harper & Row Publishers, Inc., 1989.

Deming, W. Edwards. *Out of the Crisis*. Cambridge, MA, Massachusetts Institute of Technology, Center for Advanced Engineering Study, 1982.

Drucker, Peter F. *The New Realities*. New York, Harper & Row Publishers, Inc., 1989.

Feigenbaum, Armand V. *Total Quality Control Handbook*. New York, McGraw-Hill, Inc., 1983.

Findings of the U.S. Department of Defense Technology Assessment Team on Japanese Manufacturing Technology, Final Report, CSDL = R = 2161. Washington, DC, Department of Defense, 1989.

Goldratt, Eliyahu M. and Cox, Jeff. *The Goal*. Croton-on-Hudson, New York, North River Press, 1986.

Harrington, H. James. *The Improvement Process*. New York, McGraw-Hill, Inc., 1987.

Hordeski, Michael. *Computer Integrated Manufacturing*. Blue Ridge Summit, PA, TAB Books, Inc., 1988.

IDA Report R-338, The Role of Concurrent Engineering in Weapons System Acquisition. Alexandria, VA, Institute for Defense Analysis, 1988.

Imai, Masaaki. *Kaizen*. New York, Random House, 1986.

Ishikawa, Kaoru. *Guide to Quality Control*. Tokyo, Asian Productivity Organization, 1982. U.S. distributor: New York, UNIPUB.

ISO 9001, Quality Systems—Model for quality assurance in design/development, production, installation and servicing. Geneva, International Organization for Standardization.

ISO 9002, Quality Systems—Model for quality assurance in production and installation. Geneva, International Organization for Standardization.

ISO 9003, Quality Systems—Model for quality assurance in final inspection and test. Geneva, International Organization for Standardization.

Jones, James V. *Integrated Logistics Support Handbook.* Blue Ridge Summit, PA, TAB Books, Inc., 1987.

Juran, Joseph M. *Juran on Planning for Quality.* New York, The Free Press, 1988.

Juran, Joseph M. and Gryna, Frank M., Jr. *Quality Planning and Analysis.* New York, McGraw-Hill, Inc., 1986.

King, Bob. *Better Designs in Half the Time: Implementing QFD, Quality Function Deployment, in America.* Methuen, MA, GOAL/QPC.

Kowalick, James K. *Visioneering.* New York, Alpha-Graphics Press, 1991.

_____. *Robust Design Technique: Optimizing Product, Process, and System Performance.* New York, Alpha-Graphics Press, 1991.

Lareau, William. *American Samurai.* Clinton, NJ, New Win Publishing, Inc., 1991.

Levitt, Theodore. *The Marketing Imagination.* New York, The Free Press, 1980.

Lubben, Richard T. *Just-in-Time Manufacturing.* New York, McGraw-Hill, Inc., 1988.

Mansir, Brian E. and Schacht, Nicholas R. *Continuous Improvement Process*, Report IR806R1. Bethesda, MD, Logistics Management Institute, 1989.

McGill, Michael E. *American Business and the Quick Fix.* New York, Henry Holt & Company, 1988.

Nakajima, Sceiichi. *Total Productive Maintenance.* Cambridge, MA, Productivity Press, 1988.

Office of the Assistant Secretary of Defense. *Total Quality Management: An Education and Training Strategy for Total Quality Management in the Department of Defense.* Washington, DC, Department of Defense, 1989.

Office of the Assistant Secretary of Defense for Production and Logistics. *The Role of Concurrent Engineering in Weapons System Acquisition.* Washington, DC, Department of Defense, 1988.

Office of Deputy Assistant Secretary of Defense for TQM. *Total Quality Management: A Guide for Implementation*, DoD Guide 5000.51G. Washington, DC, Department of Defense, 1989.

Peters, Thomas J. *Thriving on Chaos.* New York, Alfred A. Knopf, Inc., 1987.

Peters, Thomas J. and Waterman, Robert H., Jr. *In Search of Excellence.* New York, Harper and Row, 1982.

Ross, Phillip J. *Taguchi Techniques for Quality Engineering.* New York, McGraw-Hill, Inc., 1988.

Scherkenbach, William W. *The Deming Route to Quality and Productivity.* Washington, DC, Cee Press Books, 1988.

Scholtes, Peter R. *The Team Handbook.* Madison, WI, Joiner Associates, Inc., 1988.

Schonberger, Richard J. *World Class Manufacturing.* New York, The Free Press, 1986.

Shores, A. Richard. *Survival of the Fittest.* Milwaukee, ASQC Quality Press, 1988.

Taguchi, Genichi. *Introduction to Quality Engineering.* Tokyo, Asian Productivity Organization, 1986. Dearborn, MI, America Supplier Institute, Inc., 1986. White Plains, NY, UNIPUB/Quality Resources, 1989.

Total Quality Management Guide, Vol I and II, Final Draft. Washington, DC, Department of Defense, 1990.

Townsend, Patrick L. *Commit to Quality.* New York, John Wiley & Sons, 1986.

TQM Research Guide and Source Book. Waltham, MA, Timeplace, Inc.

Transition from Development to Production—Solving the Risk Equation, DoD 4245.7-M. Washington, DC, Department of Defense, 1985.

Wallace, Thomas E. *MRPII: Making It Happen.* Essex Junction, VT, Oliver Wright Limited Publications, Inc., 1985.

Organizations

AMERICAN MANAGEMENT ASSOCIATION
P.O. Box 319
Sarmac Lake, NY 12983

AMERICAN PRODUCTIVITY AND QUALITY CENTER (APQC)
123 North Post Oak Lane
Houston, TX 77024

AMERICAN SOCIETY FOR QUALITY CONTROL (ASQC)
310 W. Wisconsin Ave.
Milwaukee, WI 53203

AMERICAN SUPPLIER INSTITUTE
Six Parklane Blvd., Suite 411
Dearborn, MI 48120

ASSOCIATION FOR QUALITY AND PARTICIPATION
801-B W. Eighth St.
Cincinnati, OH 45203

BOOZ-ALLEN & HAMILTON
4330 East-West Highway
Bethesda, MD 20814-4455

THE BUSINESS COACH
P.O. Box 1165
Upland, CA 91785

DEFENSE SYSTEMS MANAGEMENT COLLEGE
Fort Belvoir, VA

DEFENSE TECHNICAL INFORMATION CENTER
Attn: DTIC-FDRA
Bldg. 5, Cameron Station
Alexandria, VA 22304-6145

FEDERAL QUALITY INSTITUTE
1621 N. Kent St., Room 112-RPE
Arlington, VA 22209

GOAL/QPC
13 Branch St.
Methuen, MA 01844

JURAN INSTITUTE, INC.
11 River Rd.
P.O. Box 811
Wilton, CT 06897-4469

THE LEADS CORPORATION
206 W. Sybelia Ave.
Maitland, FL 32751

LOGISTICS MANAGEMENT INSTITUTE
6400 Goldsboro Rd.
Bethesda, Md 20817-5886

MASSACHUSETTS INSTITUTE OF TECHNOLOGY
CENTER OF ADVANCED ENGINEERING STUDY
77 Massachusetts Ave.
Cambridge, MA 02139-4391

NAVAL PERSONNEL RESEARCH AND DEVELOPMENT CENTER
Code 16
San Diego, CA 92152-6800

OFFICE OF THE DEPUTY ASSISTANT SECRETARY OF DEFENSE
    FOR TOTAL QUALITY MANAGEMENT
OASD (P&L) TQM
Pentagon, Washington, DC 20301

OFFICE OF THE UNDER SECRETARY OF DEFENSE FOR ACQUISITION
    TOTAL QUALITY MANAGEMENT
ODUSD (A) TQM
Pentagon, Washington, DC 20301

PHILIP CROSBY ASSOCIATES, INC.
807 W. Morse Blvd.
P.O. Box 2369
Winter Park, FL 32790-2369

PROCESS MANAGEMENT INSTITUTE, INC.
7801 E. Bush Lake Road, Suite 360
Bloomington, MN 55435-3830

PRODUCTIVITY, INC.
P.O. Box 3007
Cambridge, MA 02140

PRODUCTIVITY, QUALITY, RESULTS
399 N. Central Avenue
Upland, CA 91786

THE SKUNKWORKS, INC.
A Tom Peters Group Company
Palo Alto, CA 94301

SOCIETY OF LOGISTICS ENGINEERS
125 W. Loop, Suite 201
Huntsville, AL 35806-1745

TIMEPLACE, INC.
460 Totten Pond Rd.
Waltham, MA 02154

TQM INSTITUTE
Irvine, CA 92714

U. S. DEPARTMENT OF COMMERCE
NATIONAL INSTITUTE OF STANDARDS AND TECHNOLOGY
The Malcolm Baldrige National Quality Award
Route 270 and Quince Orchard Rd.
Administration Building Room A537
Gaithersburg, MD 20899

Index

Other Bestsellers of Related Interest

MANAGING THE TOTAL QUALITY TRANSFORMATION—T. H. Berry

This book shows how your organization can optimize long-term profitability, competitive position, and market share by adopting a customer-focused, total quality management process (TQM). You'll learn essential techniques for implementing TQM at your company, and an array of charts, examples, and models make the information readily applicable. 256 pages, illustrated. Book No. 3924, $24.95 hardcover only

HELP WANTED: How Companies Can Survive and Thrive in the Coming Worker Shortage
—Kevin R. Hopkins, Susan L. Nestleroth, and Clint Bolick

The coming decade will be a seller's market for workers. This timely book shows you how your company can survive, and even flourish, by making sure you have the right number of workers with the right skills. You'll find step-by-step guidance on tapping new or neglected sources of workers, ways to attract and retain "non-traditional" employees, hundreds of real-world examples, suggestions for meeting the special needs of employees, strategies for on-going growth, and much more. 224 pages. Book No. 3925, $19.95 hardcover only

HOW TO GET MORE MILES PER GALLON IN THE 1990s—Robert Sikorsky

This new edition of a bestseller features a wealth of commonsense tips and techniques for improving gas mileage by as much as 100 percent. Sikorsky details specific gas-saving strategies that will greatly reduce aerodynamic drag and increase engine efficiency. New to this edition is coverage of the latest fuel-conserving automotive equipment, fuel additives, engine treatments, lubricants, and maintenance procedures that can help save energy. 184 pages, 39 illustrations. Book No. 3793, $7.95 paperback, $16.95 hardcover

EDI: What Managers Need to Know about the Revolution in Business Communications—Richard H. Baker

Implementing an effective EDI program is as much an administrative challenge as a technical one, and that's why Richard H. Baker has written this introductory guide. He describes the techniques for setting up and maintaining EDI systems, and provides guidelines for structuring your organization to take full advantage of this technology. Baker's extensive knowledge and real-world expertise make this book an absolute must for anyone trying to make sense of this rapidly changing field. 360 pages, 53 illustrations. Book No. 3724, $32.95 hardcover only

MAKING YOUR SMALL BUSINESS A SUCCESS: More Expert Advice from the U.S. Small Business Administration
—Dr. G. Howard Poteet

This informative resource compiles the advice of more than 50 national business leaders, commissioned by the Small Business Administration to produce a series of management aids for the growing entrepreneurial community. You'll get inside tips on purchasing techniques, credit and collections, performing market research, overseas marketing, consignment and mail order selling, and advertising budgets. You'll also find information on productivity improvement, quality control, inventory management, strategies for finding and paying employees, and managing employee benefit programs. 224 pages. Book No. 3718, $17.95 paperback only

DISASTER RECOVERY HANDBOOK
—Chantico Publishing Company, Inc.

Could your company survive if a tornado struck today? You'll find everything you need for coping with your worst-case scenario in this book. Among the other issues covered are plan formulation and maintenance; data, communications, and microcomputer recover procedures; and emergency procedures. Action-oriented checklists and worksheets are included to help you start planning right away—before it's too late. 276 pages, 88 illustrations. Book No. 3663, $39.95 hardcover only

VENTURING ABROAD: International Business Expansion via Joint Ventures —Jack Enen, Jr.

Now your company can position itself to take full advantage of the emerging borderless global economy, thanks to *Venturing Abroad*, the first book of its kind to actually show you how to utilize international joint ventures as a vehicle for growth in the 1990s. Jack Enen provides a wealth of concrete advice—spiced with illuminating anecdotes drawn from his more than 30 years of experience. Book No. 3653, $27.95 hardcover only

STRATEGY, SYSTEMS, AND INTEGRATION: A Handbook for Information Managers—George M. Hall

Now you can successfully plan new data processing systems and integrate existing systems. Hall shows you how you can get beyond basic strategic problems and concentrate on mastering the techniques that will meet the increasing demands of your system. From an in-depth analysis of database requirements to key management issues, you'll follow the logical order in which systems should be designed and developed. 384 pages, 118 illustrations. Book No. 3614, $39.95 hardcover only

WHEN THE BANK SAYS NO!: Creative Financing for Closely Held Businesses —Lawrence W. Tuller

The age-old maxim about banking still seems to be true: If you don't need money, any bank will lend it; if you do need money, no one is interested. *When the Bank Says No!* examines more than 20 different varieties, sources, and methods of financing alternatives—alternatives that yield more cash at lower risk—and most at lower cost—than banks can match. Now, your company—no matter what its size—can use Tuller's advice to free itself from the handcuffs of bank debt. 320 pages, illustrated. Book No. 3590, $22.95 hardcover only

SELLING TO THE GIANTS: How to Become a Key Supplier to Large Corporations—Jeffrey P. Davidson, CMC, MBA, and George-Anne Fay

Here are guidelines for successfully marketing goods or services to the nation's largest buyers. Discover how to develop and maintain profitable, long-term business relationships. You'll cover such important areas as: finding a profitable niche, developing marketing strategies, mastering selling techniques, understanding the corporate purchasing psyche, creating marketing presentations, using trade shows as a marketing tool, and becoming a successful bidder. 206 pages, illustrated. Book No. 3586, $14.95 paperback, $27.95 hardcover

TRADE SHOW EXHIBITING: The Insider's Guide for Entrepreneurs —Diane K. Weintraub

Now any size company can enjoy trade show success, thanks to this no-nonsense guide. This book gives you the map for bottom-line trade-show success. First, the author shows you the most direct way to increase profits so that you aren't wasting time on efforts that don't work. Second, you'll get a look at possible pitfalls to avoid. 224 pages, 24 illustrations. Book No. 3585, $14.95 paperback, $29.95 hardcover

RIP-OFF TIP-OFFS: Winning the Auto Repair Game—Robert Sikorsky

Don't get ripped off when you take your car for repairs. This book gives you the ammunition to stop repair scams before they start. Sikorsky exposes popular tactics used by cheats and describes how to ensure a fair deal. If you have been ripped off, he tells you who to complain effectively—both to get your money back and to put the charlatans out of business for good. But most importantly, Sikorsky tells how to avoid getting burned in the first place by learning how your car works and by keeping it in good condition. 140 pages, 29 illustrations. Book No. 3572, $9.95 paperback, $16.95 hardcover